WILDCAT AND THE ACORNS
and other stories

WILDCAT
AND
THE ACORNS
and other stories

KENJI MIYAZAWA

Translated by
JOHN BESTER

KODANSHA
KODANSHA INTERNATIONAL

Published by Kodansha Publishers Ltd., 12-
21, Otowa 2-chome, Bunkyo-ku, Tokyo 112,
and Kodansha International Ltd., 17-14,
Otowa 1-chome, Bunkyo-ku, Tokyo 112.
English translation copyright © 1972 by
Kodansha International Ltd. All rights
reserved. Printed in Japan.
ISBN 4-06-186015-1
First edition, 1985
Eighth printing, 1996

CONTENTS

1

THE BEARS OF
MT. NAMETOKO

The bears of Mt. Nametoko are worth hearing about. Mt. Nametoko is a large mountain, and the Fuchizawa River starts somewhere inside it. On most days of the year, Mt. Nametoko breathes in and breathes out cold mists and clouds. The mountains all about it, too, are like blackish green sea slugs or bald sea goblins. Halfway up the mountain there yawns a great cave, from which the river Fuchizawa falls suddenly some three hundred feet in a waterfall that goes thundering down through the thick-growing cypresses and maples.

Nowadays nobody walks along the old Nakayama Highway, so it is all grown over with butterbur and knotweed, and there are places where people have put up fences on the track to stop cattle from getting away and climbing up the mountains. But if you push your way for about six miles through the rustling undergrowth, you will hear in the distance a sound like the wind on a mountaintop. If you peer carefully in that direction, you might be puzzled by something long, white, and narrow that comes falling down the mountain in a flurry of mist. That is the Ozora Falls of Mt. Nametoko. And in that area, they say, there used to be any number of bears. To tell the truth, I myself have never seen either Mt. Nametoko or the liver of a newly killed bear. This is all what I have heard from others, or worked out for myself. It may not be entirely true, but I, at least, believe it.

What is certain, at any rate, is that Mt. Nametoko is famous for its bear's liver. It is good for the stomachache and it helps wounds heal. At the entrance to the Namari hot springs there is a sign that says "Bear's Liver From Mt. Nametoko." So it is certain that there are bears on Mt. Nametoko. I can almost see them, going across the valleys with their pink tongues lolling out, and the bear cubs wrestling with each other till finally they lose their tempers and box each other's ears. It was those same bears that the celebrated bear hunter Kojuro Fuchizawa once killed so freely.

Kojuro Fuchizawa was a swarthy, well-knit, middle-aged man with a squint. His body was massive, like a small barrel, and his hands were as big and thick as the handprint of the god Bishamon that they use to cure people's sicknesses at the Kitajima Shrine. In summer, he wore a cape made of bark to keep off the rain, with leggings, and he carried a woodsman's axe and a gun as big and heavy as an old-fashioned blunderbuss. With his great yellow hound, he would crisscross the mountains from Mt. Nametoko to Shidoke Valley, from Mitsumata to Mt. Sakkai, from Mamiana Wood to Shira Valley.

When he went up the old, dried-up valleys, the trees grew so thickly that it was like going through a shadowy green tunnel, though sometimes it suddenly became bright with green and gold, and at other times sunlight fell all around as though the whole place had burst into bloom. Kojuro walked slowly and ponderously, as completely at home as though he were in his own living room. The hound ran on ahead, scampering along high banks or plunging into the water. He would swim for all he was worth across the sluggish, faintly menacing backwaters, then, when he finally reached the other side, would shake himself vigorously to get the water out of his coat and stand with nose wrinkled waiting for his master to catch up. Kojuro would come across with his mouth slightly twisted, moving his legs stiffly and cautiously like a pair of compasses, while the water splashed up above his knees in a white frieze. And I should also add that the bears in the area of Mt. Nametoko were fond of Kojuro.

One proof of this is that they would often look down in silence from some high place as Kojuro squelched his way up the valleys or went along the narrow ledges, all grown over with thistles, that bordered the valley. Clinging to a branch at the top of a tree or sitting on the top of a bank with their paws round their knees, they would watch with interest as he went by.

The bears even seemed to like Kojuro's hound.

Yet for all that, they did not like it much when they really came up against Kojuro, and the dog flew at them like a ball of fire, or when Kojuro with a strange glint in his eyes leveled his gun at them. At such times, most bears would wave their paws as though in distress, telling him that they did not want to be treated in that way.

But there are all kinds of bears, just as there are all kinds of people, and the fiercest of them would rear up on their hind legs with a great roar and advance on Kojuro with both paws stretched out, ignoring the dog as though they could crush it underfoot as easily as that. Kojuro would remain perfectly calm and, taking aim at the center of the bear's forehead from behind a tree, would let fly with his gun.

The whole forest would seem to cry out loud, and the bear would slump to the ground. The dark red blood would gush from its mouth, it would snuffle rapidly, and it would die.

Then Kojuro would stand his gun against a tree, cautiously go up to the bear, and say something like this:

"Don't think I killed you out of hatred, Bear. I have to make a living, just as you have to be shot. I'd like to do different work, work with no sin attached, but I've no fields, and they say my trees belong to the authorities, and when I go into the village nobody will have anything to do with me. I'm a hunter because I can't help it. It's fate that made you a bear, and it's fate that makes me do this work. Make sure you're not reborn as a bear next time!"

At such times the dog, too, would sit by him with narrowed eyes and a dejected air.

The dog, you see, was Kojuro's sole companion. In the summer of his fortieth year, his whole family had fallen sick with dysentery, and his son and his son's wife had died. The dog, however, had remained healthy and vigorous.

Next, Kojuro would take out of his pocket a short, razor-sharp knife and in one long stroke slit the bear's skin open from under its chin down to its chest and on to its belly. The scene that followed I don't care to think about. Either way, in the end Kojuro would put the bright red bear's liver in the wooden chest on his back, wash the fur that was all in dripping, bloody tassels in the river, roll it up, put it on his back, and set off down the valley with a heavy heart.

It even seemed to Kojuro that he could understand what the bears were saying to each other. Early one spring, before any of the trees had turned green, Kojuro took the dog with him and went far up the marshy bed of Shira Valley. As dusk drew near, he started to climb up to the pass leading over to Bakkai Valley, where he had built a small hut of bamboo grass to shelter in. But for some unexplained reason Kojuro, unlike his accustomed self, took the wrong trail. Any number of times he started up, then came down and started up again; even the dog was quite exhausted, and Kojuro himself was breathing heavily out of one side of his mouth before they finally found the previous year's hut, which was half tumbled down.

Remembering that there had been a spring just below the hut, Kojuro started off down the mountain, but had only gone a little way when to his surprise he came across two bears, a mother and a cub barely a year old, standing in the faint light of the still new moon, staring intently at the other side of the valley with their paws up to their foreheads, just as a human being does when he is looking into the distance. To Kojuro it seemed almost that the two bears were surrounded by a kind of halo, and he stopped and stared at them transfixed.

Then the small bear said in a wheedling voice, "I'm sure it's snow, Mother. Only the near side of the valley is white, isn't it? Yes, I'm sure it's snow, Mother!"

The mother bear went on staring intently for a while, then said finally, "It's not snow. It wouldn't fall just in that one place."

"Then it must have been left there after the rest melted," said the cub.

"No, I went past there only yesterday on my way to look at the thistle buds."

Kojuro stared hard in the same direction. The moonlight was gliding bluish white down the mountainside, which was shining like a silver helmet. After a while the cub spoke again.

"If it's not snow then it must be frost. I'm sure it is."

There really will be a frost tonight, thought Kojuro to himself. A star was shimmering blue close to the moon; even the color of the moon itself was just like ice.

"I know what it is," said the mother bear. "It's cherry blossoms."

"Is that all? I know all about that."

"No, you've never seen it."

"But I *do* know it. I went and brought some home myself the other day."

"No—that wasn't cherry. It was Indian bean you brought home, I think."

"Really?" the cub said innocently.

For some reason, Kojuro's heart felt full. He gave a last glance at the flowers like snow on the far side of the valley, and at the mother bear and her cub standing bathed in the moonlight, then stealthily, taking care to make no sound, set off back. As he slowly withdrew, praying all the while that the wind would not blow his scent in their direction, the fragrance of spicebush came sharply to him on the moonlight.

Yet how pitifully humbled was that same brave Kojuro when he went to town to sell the bearskins and the bear liver.

Somewhere near the center of the town there was a large hardware store where winnowing baskets and sugar, whetstones and cheap cigarettes, and even glass fly traps were set out for sale.

Kojuro had only to step over the threshold of the shop with the great bundle of bearskins on his back for the people there to start smiling as though to say, "Here he is again." The master of the shop would be seated massively beside a large brazier in a room leading off the shop.

"Thank you for your kindness last time, sir." And the same Kojuro who back in the hills was so completely his own master would set down his bundle of skins and, kneeling on the boards, bow deferentially.

"Well, well . . . and what can I do for you today?"

"I've brought along a few bearskins again."

"Bearskins? The last ones are still lying around somewhere in the store. We don't need any today."

"Don't be so difficult. Please buy some. I'll let you have them cheap."

"However cheap they are, I don't want them," the master of the shop would say with perfect composure, tapping out the small bowl of his pipe against the palm of his hand.

Whenever he heard this, Kojuro, brave lord of the hills, would feel his face twist with anxiety.

At Kojuro's home they could find chestnuts in the hills, and millet would grow in the apology for a field that lay at the back of the house; but no rice would grow, nor was there any soybean paste for making soup. So he must have some rice, however little, to take back for the family of seven—his old mother and his grandchildren.

If he had lived down in the village, he would have grown hemp for weaving cloth, but at Kojuro's place nothing grew but a few wisteria vines, which were woven into baskets and the like.

After a while, Kojuro would say in a voice hoarse with distress, "Please—please buy some, whatever the price." And Kojuro would actually bow to him again.

The shopkeeper would puff smoke for a while without saying anything, then, concealing a slight grin of satisfaction, would seat himself in front of Kojuro and hand him four large silver coins. Kojuro would accept with a grin and raise them respectfully to his forehead. Then the master of the shop would gradually unbend.

"Here—give Kojuro some saké."

By now Kojuro would be glowing with delight. The shopkeeper would talk to him at leisure of this and that. Very deferentially, Kojuro would tell him of things back in the hills. Soon, word would come from the kitchen that the saké was ready. Kojuro would half make to go, but in the end would be dragged off to the kitchen, where he would go through his polite greetings again.

Almost immediately, they would bring a small black lacquered table bearing slices of salted salmon with chopped cuttlefish and a china bottle of warm saké.

Kojuro would seat himself very correctly and formally before the table. Then he would start to eat, balancing the pieces of cuttlefish on the back of his hand before gulping them down and reverently pouring the yellowish saké into the tiny cup.

However low prices might be, anyone would have agreed that two yen was too little for a pair of bearskins.

It was really too little, and Kojuro knew it. Why, then, did Kojuro not sell his skins to someone other than that hardware dealer? To most people, it would be a mystery. But in those days there was an order of things—it was laid down that Kojuro should get the better of the bears, that the shopkeeper should get the better of Kojuro, and that the bears—but since the shopkeeper lived in the town, the bears did not get the better of him, for the moment at least.

Such being the state of affairs, Kojuro killed the bears without any feeling of hatred for them. One year, though, a strange thing happened.

Kojuro was squelching his way up a valley and had climbed onto a rock to look about him when he saw a large bear, its back hunched, clambering like a cat up a tree directly in front of him. Immediately, Kojuro leveled his gun. The dog, delighted, was already at the foot of the tree, rushing round and round it madly.

But the bear, who for a while seemed to be debating whether he should come down and set on Kojuro or let himself be shot where he was, suddenly let go with his paws and came crashing down to the ground. Immediately on his guard, Kojuro put his gun to his shoulder and went closer as though to shoot. But at this point the bear put up its paws and shouted, "What are you after? Why do you have to shoot me?"

"For nothing but your fur and your liver," said Kojuro. "Not that I shall get any great sum for them when I take them to town. I'm very sorry for you, but it just can't be helped. But when I hear you say that kind of thing, I almost feel I'd rather live on chestnuts and ferns and the like, even if it killed me."

"Won't you wait two more years? For myself, I don't care whether I die or not, but there are still things I must do, so wait just two years. When two years are up, you'll find me dead in front of your house without fail. You can have my fur and my insides too."

Filled with an odd emotion, Kojuro stood quite still, thinking.

The bear got its four paws firmly on the ground and began, ever so slowly, to walk. But still Kojuro went on standing there, staring vacantly in front of him.

Slowly, slowly, the bear walked away without looking back, as though it knew very well that Kojuro would never let fly suddenly from behind. For a moment, its broad, brownish black back shone bright in the sunlight falling through the branches of the trees, and at that same moment Kojuro gave a painful groan and, crossing the valley, made for home.

It was just two years later. One morning, the wind blew so fiercely that Kojuro, sure that it was blowing down trees and hedge and all, went outside to see. The cypress hedge was standing untouched, but at its foot there lay something brownish black that he had seen before. His heart gave a turn, for it was just two years, and he had been feeling worried in case the bear should come along. He went up to it, and found the bear he had met that day, lying there as it had promised, dead, in a great pool of blood that had gushed from its mouth. Almost unconsciously, Kojuro pressed his hands together in prayer.

It was one day in January. As Kojuro was leaving home that morning, he said something he had never said before.

"Mother, I must be getting old. This morning, for the first time in my life, I don't feel I want to wade through the streams."

Kojuro's mother of ninety-one, who sat spinning on the veranda in the sun, raised her rheumy eyes and glanced at Kojuro with an expression that might have been either tearful or smiling.

Kojuro tied on his straw sandals, heaved himself

to his feet, and set off. One after the other the children poked their faces out of the barn and said smiling, "Come home soon, Grandpa."

Kojuro looked up at the smooth, bright blue sky, then turned to his grandchildren and said, "I'll be back later."

He climbed up through the pure white, close-packed snow in the direction of Shira Valley. The dog was already panting heavily, its pink tongue lolling out as it ran ahead and stopped, ran ahead and stopped again. Very soon Kojuro's figure sank out of sight beyond a low hill, and the children returned to their games.

Kojuro followed the bank of the river up the Shira Valley. Here the water lay in deep blue pools, there it was frozen into sheets of glass, here the icicles hung in countless numbers like bead curtains, and from both banks the berries of the spindle tree peered out like red and yellow flowers. As he climbed upstream, Kojuro saw his own glittering shadow and the dog's, deep indigo and sharply etched on the snow, mingling as they moved with the shadows of the birch trunks.

On the other side of the summit from Shira Valley there lived, as he had confirmed during the summer, a large bear.

On he went upstream, fording five small tributaries that came flowing into the valley, crossing the water again and again from right to left and from left to right. He came to a small waterfall, from the foot of which he began to climb up towards the ridge. The snow was so dazzling it seemed to be on fire, and as he toiled upward, Kojuro felt as if he had purple glasses before his eyes.

The dog was climbing as though determined that the steepness of the slope would not beat him, clinging grimly to the snow, though he nearly slipped many times. When they finally reached the top they found themselves on a plateau that sloped gently away, where the snow sparkled like white marble and snow-covered peaks thrust up into the sky all about them.

It happened as Kojuro was taking a rest there at the summit. Suddenly, the dog began to bark frantically. Startled, Kojuro looked behind him and saw the same great bear that he had glimpsed that summer rearing up on its hind legs and bearing down on him. Without panic, Kojuro planted his feet firmly in the snow and took aim.

Raising its two massive front paws, the bear came rushing straight at him. Even Kojuro turned rather pale at the sight.

Kojuro heard the crack of the gun. Yet the bear showed no sign of falling, but seemed to come swaying on towards him, black and raging like a storm. The dog sank his teeth into its leg. The next moment, a great noise filled Kojuro's head and everything about him went white. Then, far off in the distance, he heard a voice saying, "Ah, Kojuro, I didn't mean to kill you."

"This is death," thought Kojuro. All about him he could see lights twinkling incessantly like blue stars. "Those are the signs that I'm dead," he thought, "the fires you see when you die. Forgive me, bears." As for what he felt from then on, I have no idea.

It was the evening of the third day following. A moon hung in the sky like a great ball of ice. The snow was a bright bluish white, and the water gave off a phosphorescent glow. The Pleiades and Orion's belt twinkled now green, now orange, as though they were breathing.

On the plateau on top of the mountain, surrounded by chestnut trees and snowy peaks, many great black shapes were gathered in a ring, each casting its own black shadow, each prostrate in the snow like a Muslim at prayer, never moving. And there at the highest point one might have seen, by the light of the snow and the moon, Kojuro's corpse set in a kneeling position. One might even have imagined that on his dead, frozen face one could see a chill smile as though he were still alive. Orion's belt moved to the center of the heavens, it tilted still further to the west, yet the great black shapes stayed quite still, as though they had turned to stone.

2

THE SPIDER,
THE SLUG, AND
THE RACCOON

A red spider with long arms and a silver-colored slug and a raccoon who had never washed his face all started at the Badger School together. There were three things that Mr. Badger taught.

First, he taught about the race between the tortoise and the hare. Next, he taught that, as this showed, it was up to everyone to overtake his fellows and become bigger and more important than they. The third thing was that the biggest person was the most worthy of all.

From then on the three of them worked with all their might, vying with each other to be top of the class.

In the first grade, the slug and raccoon were punished for always being late, so the spider came out on top. The slug and the raccoon shed tears of mortification.

In the second grade, Mr. Badger made a mistake in calculating his marks, so the slug came first. The spider and the raccoon ground their teeth in mortification.

In the third-grade examination, the light was so bright that it made Mr. Badger's eyes water and he kept shutting them. So the raccoon looked into the textbook as he wrote the answers and came first.

Thus the red spider with long arms and the silver slug and the raccoon who had never washed his face all graduated from Mr. Badger's school at the same time.

The three of them, who were very good friends on the surface, did all kinds of things to mark the occasion. They held a party for Mr. Badger to thank him for his kindness, followed by a special farewell party for themselves, but deep in their hearts they were all busy thinking about one another and saying to themselves, "Pooh! And what good do they think *they* are? Just wait and see who becomes the biggest and most important!"

Once the meetings were over, they all went back to their own homes to put the things they had learned into practice. Mr. Badger was already busy again, chasing a sewer rat every day in order to enroll him in school.

Just about this time the dogtooth violets were in bloom, and innumerable blue-eyed bees were flying about cheerfully, buzzing in the sunlight, giving greetings to each small flower in turn before they took its honey and scent, or carrying the golden balls of pollen to other flowers in return, or collecting the wax that the new buds on the trees had no more need of, so as to build their six-sided homes. It was a busy, cheerful day at the beginning of spring.

What Befell the Spider

The evening after the parties were over the spider came back to the oak tree where he lived at the entrance to the wood.

Unfortunately, he had used up all his money at the Badger School, and he had not a single thing of his own. So he put up with his hunger and began to spin a web beneath the dim light of the moon.

He was so hungry that he had hardly any web left in his body. But he muttered to himself, "They'll see! They'll see!" and spun out the thread for all he was worth, till at last he had spun a web about as big as a small copper coin. Then he hid himself behind a branch and all night long peered out at the web with gleaming eyes.

Around dawn, a baby horsefly came flying along humming to himself and ran into the web. But the spider had been so hungry when he spun the web that the thread was not a bit sticky, and the baby horsefly had soon broken it and was making to fly away.

Quite beside himself, the spider rushed out from behind the branch and sank his teeth into the horsefly.

"Mercy! Mercy!" wept the little horsefly piteously, but without saying anything the spider ate him up, head, wings, feet, and all. He heaved a satisfied sigh and for a while lay looking up at the sky and rubbing his belly, then he produced a little more thread. So the web grew one size bigger.

The spider went back behind the branch, and his six eyes gleamed bright as he sat motionless, watching the web.

"Where would this be, now?" inquired a blind mayfly who came along, walking with the aid of a stick.

"This is an inn, sir," said the spider, blinking all his six eyes separately.

The mayfly seated himself in the web with an air of weariness. The spider ran out.

"Here's some tea for you," he said, and without warning sank his teeth into the mayfly's body.

The mayfly raised the hand with which he had been going to take the tea and threshed about helplessly, at the same time beginning to recite in a piteous voice:

> Ah, pity on my daughter when
> The dreadful tidings drear . . .

"Here, that's enough of that row! Stop your struggling!" said the spider, whereupon the mayfly pressed his palms together and entreated him, "Have pity, kind sir. Pray wait a while, that I may recite my last poem."

"All right, but be quick!" said the spider, feeling a little sorry for him. And he waited, keeping a firm grip on the mayfly's legs.

The mayfly began to recite in a truly pitiful, tiny voice, going back to the beginning of the poem and starting all over again:

> Ah, pity on my daughter when
> The dreadful tidings drear
> Of parent's doom so far from home
> Shall reach her sorrowing ear!
> Most pitiful a pilgrim's staff
> She'll take in her small hand,
> And on a weary pilgrimage

She'll set off through the land.
A-wandering from door to door
Through wind and rain she goes.
"Oh, give me alms," she begs, "that I
May pray his soul's repose."
Dear Daughter, be forewarned and shun
The cruel spider's lair.
Of this my last advice take heed—
Of webby inns beware!

"Enough of your impudence!" exclaimed the spider, and swallowed the mayfly in one gulp. For a while he lay looking up at the sky and rubbing his belly, then he gave a wink, sang playfully to himself, "Now your days of impudence are over," and started spinning thread again.

The web grew three sizes larger, so that it was like a splendid, large umbrella. Quite easy in his mind by now, the spider hid himself again in the leaves. Just then, he heard someone singing in a pleasant voice down below:

O, the red long-legged spider
Crawls about up in the sky
As he lets out, soft and bright,
His silver thread of light
In a shining web spun high.

He looked and saw it was a pretty female spider.

"Come up here," said the long-legged spider, letting a long, long thread of web down for her.

The female spider got hold of it at once and came climbing up. So the two of them became man and wife. There were all kinds of things to eat in the web every day, and the wife spider ate a great deal and turned it all into babies. So lots of baby spiders were born. But they were all so small you could hardly see them.

It was terribly lively, with the children sliding on the web, and wrestling, and swinging. And best of all, the dragonfly came one day and informed them that the insects had passed a resolution making the spider vice-president of the Society of Insects and Worms.

One day, the spider and his wife were hidden in the leaves drinking tea when they heard someone singing down below in a conceited voice:

O, the red long-legged spider,
Of sons he had ten score,
But the biggest of them all
Was incredibly small—
Like a grain of sand, no more.

They looked and found it was the silver slug, who had grown tremendously big since they last saw him.

The spider's good lady was so put out that she cried and cried and would not be consoled.

But the long-legged spider sniffed and said, "He's jealous of me these days, that's what. Ho! Slug—I'm being made vice-president of the Society of Insects and Worms! How d'you like that, eh? I can't see the likes of you doing that, however fat you may get. Ha, ha, ha, ha!"

The slug was so furious that he came down with a fever for several days and could say nothing but, "Ah, that cursed spider! Such an insult! That cursed spider!"

From time to time the web would break in the wind or would be damaged by some lout of a stag beetle, but the spider soon spun out a smooth length of thread and mended it again.

Of their two hundred children, a full one hundred and ninety-eight were carried off by ants, or disappeared without trace, or died of dysentery. But the children were all so much alike that their parents soon forgot all about them.

And the web by now was a magnificent affair. A steady stream of insects got caught in it.

One day, the spider and his wife were again hidden in the leaves drinking tea when a traveling mosquito came flying along, took one look at the web, and flew away again in alarm. The spider put three of its legs out into the net and watched in disgust as it went.

Just then, a great peal of laughter came from down below, and a rich voice began to sing:

> O, red long-legged spider,
> Long-legged spider red—
> Your web is such a poor affair
> The traveling mosquito there
> Just hummed and turned his head.

It was the raccoon who had never washed his face.

"You wait, fool Raccoon!" said the spider, gnashing his teeth in rage. "Before long I'll be president of the Society of Insects and Worms and then I'll have you bowing to me—you wait and see!"

From then on, the spider set to work furiously. He spun a full ten webs in different places and kept watch over them even at night.

But sad to tell, the rot set in. So much food piled up that in time things began to go bad. And the rot spread to the spider and his wife and their children. All four of them began to rot and turn soggy, beginning at the ends of their legs, till one day they were finally washed away by the rain.

This was around the time when the pearlwort was in bloom, and the many blue-eyed bees had scattered over the countryside, where they gathered the honey from each small flower as though taking fire from small handlamps.

What Befell the Silver Slug

Around the time when the spider spun his copper-coin web on the oak tree at the entrance to the wood, a stag beetle turned up at the silver slug's fine residence.

By then, the slug had quite a reputation in the wood. He was educated, everyone said, and he was good-natured and considerate to others.

"Slug," said the stag beetle, "I'm going through hard times now. There's nothing for me to eat, and no water, so I wonder if you'd let me have just a little of the butterbur juice you've got stored?"

"Why, of course I will," said the slug. "Come inside, won't you?"

"That's very kind of you. You're a friend in need," said the stag beetle as he gulped down the butterbur juice.

"Have some more," said the slug. "Why, in a way we're brothers. Ho, ho, ho! Come on, now, just a little more."

"Well, then, perhaps just a little. Thank you, thank you." And the stag beetle drank a little more.

"Beetle," said the slug, "when you feel better, shall we have a little wrestle? We haven't wrestled for ages. Ho, ho, ho! Not for ages."

"I'm too starved to have the strength," said the stag beetle.

"Then I'll give you something to eat. Here, help yourself," said the slug, getting out some thistle buds and the like.

"Most kind. Since you insist then . . ." And the beetle ate them.

"Now let's wrestle. Ho, ho, ho!" said the slug, getting up as he spoke.

"I'm rather weak," said the stag beetle, getting up reluctantly, "so please don't throw me too heavily."

"Heave-ho! There!" The beetle hit the ground with a crash. "Once more, eh? Ho, ho, ho!"

"No, I'm tired now."

"Oh, come on! Heave-ho! There! Ho, ho, ho!" Again the beetle crashed to the floor.

"Once more. Ho, ho, ho!"

"No, I've had enough."

"Come on, now, just once. Heave-ho! Oh, ho, ho, ho . . ." Crash went the beetle again.

"Once more. Ho, ho, ho!"

"No, I'm . . ."

"Oh, come on! Heave-ho! Ho, ho, ho, ho!" Crash went the beetle.

"Once more."

"I'm dying. Goodbye."

"Come on, now. Just once. Ho, ho, ho. . . . Come now, on your feet! Here, let me help you up. Heave-ho! There! Ho, ho, ho, ho . . ."

And the beetle died. So the silver slug munched

him down, the hard outside parts and all.

About a month after that, a lizard came limping along to the slug's splendid residence.

"Slug," he said, "I wonder if I could have a little medicine today?"

"What's wrong?" asked the slug with a smile.

"I've been bitten by a snake," said the lizard.

"Oh, that's easy," said the slug, smiling. "I'll just give it a little lick for you. If I lick it the snake poison will soon disappear. It ought to, seeing that I can dissolve the snake itself. Ho, ho, ho!"

"I'd be most grateful, then," said the lizard, putting out his leg.

"Why, of course, of course. We're brothers in a way, aren't we? And so are you and the snake, eh? Ho, ho, ho!" And the slug put his mouth to the lizard's wound.

"Thank you, Slug," said the lizard after a while.

"I must lick it some more yet, or you'll suffer later. I won't make it better if you come here asking again. Ho, ho, ho!" mumbled the slug indistinctly as he went on licking the lizard.

"Slug," said the lizard in alarm, "I do believe my leg's starting to dissolve!"

"Ho, ho, ho! Why, it's nothing much," replied the slug indistinctly as before. "Ho, ho, ho!"

"Slug—" said the lizard anxiously, "I'm feeling kind of hot around the middle."

"Ho, ho, ho!" mumbled the slug. "Why, it's nothing to fuss about."

"Slug," cried the lizard tearfully, "I do believe my body's half melted away. Stop now, please!"

"Ho, ho, ho! Why, it's nothing much at all," said the slug. "Just a very little. Ho, ho, ho!"

As he heard this, the lizard stopped worrying at last. He stopped worrying because it was just at that moment that his heart melted.

So the slug slupped up the lizard completely. And he became quite ridiculously big. He had felt so pleased with himself that he hadn't been able to resist teasing the spider.

But the spider had taunted him in return, so that he had taken to his bed with a fever, and day after day he would say, "You just see. I'll get as big as I can, then I'll almost certainly be made an honorary member of the Society of Insects and Worms. And if the spider says anything, I won't answer but just give him a contemptuous sniff."

In fact, though, the slug's reputation, for some reason or other, began to decline just around then.

The raccoon in particular would always pooh-pooh any mention of the slug, saying with a smile, "I can't say I think much of the slug's way of doing things. Why, anybody could get big the way he does it!"

When the slug heard this he got still angrier and tried frantically to find ways of becoming an honorary society member as soon as possible.

Before long the spider rotted and dissolved and was washed away in the rain so the slug felt a bit easier, though he was still waiting eagerly for someone to turn up.

Then one day a frog came along.

"Good day, Slug," he said. "Could you let me have a little water?"

"Nice to see you, Frog," said the slug in a determinedly pleasant voice, since he was longing to slup up the frog. "Water? As much as you like. There's been quite a drought lately, but you and I are brothers in a way, aren't we? Ho, ho, ho!" He took the frog to the water jar.

The frog drank his fill, then he looked at the slug for a while with an innocent expression and said, "Slug, shall we have a wrestle?"

The slug was delighted. The frog had made the very suggestion that he had been about to make himself. A feeble creature like the frog would probably be ready for slupping up after five throws or so.

"Let's," he said. "Heave-ho! There! Ho, ho, ho!" The frog was dashed to the ground.

"Let's try again. Heave-ho! There! Ho, ho, ho!" Again the frog was thrown.

At this point the frog hastily got a bag of salt out of his pocket.

"Sumo wrestlers always purify the ring with salt,"

he said. "There!" And the ground all about was scattered with white salt.

"Frog," said the slug, "I'm sure you'll beat me next time. You're strong. Heave-ho! There! Ho, ho, ho!" The frog was dashed to the ground.

He lay there spread-eagled, with his green belly turned up to the sky as though he were dead. The silver slug made to go to slup him up, but for some reason he couldn't move his legs. He looked, and found they were half dissolved.

"Heavens! The salt!" cried the slug.

At this the frog leaped up and, seating himself cross-legged on the ground, opened wide his great holdall of a mouth and laughed.

"Goodbye, Slug," he said with a bow. "This is most distressing for you."

The slug was nearly in tears.

"Frog," he said. "Goo . . ." But just then his tongue dissolved.

The frog laughed and laughed.

"I expect you were going to say goodbye," he said. "Well, goodbye to you then. When I get home, I'll have a good cry for you." And off he sped without looking back once.

The white flowers of the buckwheat sown in autumn were just beginning to bloom, and the countless blue-eyed bees were moving about among the pinkish stalks that filled the square field, swaying on the tiny branches that bore the flowers, busily gathering the last honey of the year.

What Befell the Raccoon

The raccoon did not wash his face on purpose.

By the time the spider had spun his first web the size of a copper coin on the oak at the entrance to the wood, the raccoon was back at the temple where he lived in the country. But he, too, was quite starved, and he was leaning against a pine tree with his eyes closed when a rabbit came along.

"Raccoon," the rabbit said, "it's dreadful to be hungry like this. One might as well die and have done with it."

"Yes indeed," said the raccoon. "It's all up with us. But it is the will of Wildcat, the Blessed Feline. Ah, Ave Feles, Ave Feles!"

The rabbit joined him in reciting the Ave Feles.

"Ave Feles, Ave Feles, Ave Feles!" The raccoon took the rabbit's paw and drew him a little closer.

"Ave Feles, Ave Feles," murmured the raccoon. "Everything is the will of the Blessed Feline. Ave Feles, Ave Feles . . ." And he took a bite of the rabbit's ear.

"Ouch!" cried the rabbit in alarm. "Raccoon, what are you doing?"

"Ave Feles, Ave Feles," mumbled the raccoon, his mouth full of the rabbit's ear. "Everything on earth is ordained by the will of Wildcat. Ah, the ineffable wisdom that decrees that I should chew your ears down to a reasonable size! Ave Feles! . . ." And he finished by eating up both the rabbit's ears.

As he listened, the rabbit was gradually filled with joy and began to shed great tears.

"Ave Feles, Ave Feles! Ah, blessed be Wildcat! Ah, how great a love that troubles itself even with the ears of such a wretch as I! What are two ears, or more, if only one be saved? Ave Feles!"

The raccoon, too, shed great false tears.

"Ave Feles, Ave Feles! Thou sayest to chew the rabbit's legs this time? That would be because he jumps too much, perhaps. Yes, yes—I chew, I chew! Ave Feles, Ave Feles! Thy will be done!" And he took a good mouthful of the rabbit's back legs.

"Ah, praise be!" cried the rabbit ever more joyfully. "Thanks to you, Wildcat, my back legs are gone and I need walk no more! Ah, praise be! Ave Feles, Ave Feles!"

The raccoon was pretending to cry as though his whole body would soon be soaked in tears.

"Ave Feles, Ave Feles! Everything is according to thy will. So thou sayest that a humble creature such as I must live on to carry out thy will? Very well, very well, if such be thy will . . . Ave Feles, Ave Feles, Ave Feles! Thy will be done. Mumble, munch . . ."

The rabbit disappeared completely.

"You cheated me!" he called from the raccoon's stomach. "Your stomach is pitch dark! Ah, what a fool I was!"

"Stop that row!" said the raccoon angrily. "Hurry up and get digested!"

"Listen everybody!" the rabbit called again. "Don't be tricked by the raccoon!"

Peering anxiously around, the raccoon shut his mouth and kept it like that for a while, covering his nose with his paw at the same time so that the sound could not get out.

Just two months after this, the raccoon was performing the devotions as usual at his house when a wolf came carrying half a bushel of unhulled rice and begged him for a sermon.

"The lives that you have taken," began the raccoon, "will not be easily atoned for. What living creature is there that dies willingly? But you ate them, did you not? Make haste to repent, else dire torment awaits you! Ah how fearful! Ave Feles, Ave Feles!"

Terrified out of his wits, the wolf stared anxiously about him. "Then what do you think I should do?" he asked.

"I am the representative of the Blessed Feline," said the raccoon. "So you must do as I say. Ave Feles, Ave Feles!"

"What must I do?" asked the wolf in alarm.

"Well, now," said the raccoon, "just stay still, and

I'll take your fangs out. Ah, how many innocent lives have these fangs taken! A fearful thing. Now I'll gouge out your eyes. How many creatures have these eyes stared into death! A dreadful thought. And now (Ave Feles, Ave Feles, Ave Feles!) I'll just chew your ears a little. This is by way of punishment. Ave Feles! Ave Feles! Bear up, now. Now I'll chew your head. Mumble, mumble. Ave Feles! The important thing in this world is endurance. Ave . . . mumble, munch. . . . Now I'll eat your legs. Very tasty. Ave Feles, munch, mumble. Now your back . . . mm, this is good too. Mumble, mumble, munch, munch . . ."

In the end, the wolf was eaten up entirely. And he called out from inside the raccoon's stomach, "It's pitch dark in here. But here are some rabbit's bones. Who could have killed him? Whoever you are, I expect you'll be chewed up while listening to a sermon by the raccoon."

"You make too much noise," said the raccoon. "I must put a lid on you." And he swallowed whole the bundle containing half a bushel of rice that the wolf had brought with him.

The next day, though, the raccoon just didn't feel at all well. For some reason, his stomach hurt dreadfully, and he had a pricking feeling in his throat.

At first he eased the pain by drinking water, but it grew worse each successive day, till in the end he was beside himself with pain.

Finally, on the twenty-fifth day after he had eaten the wolf, the raccoon whose body was swollen up like a rubber balloon by now, burst open with a great boom.

When all the animals in the wood gathered in alarm, they found that the raccoon's body was stuffed with rice plants. The rice that the raccoon had swallowed had sprouted and grown.

Mr. Badger came too, a little late. He took a look and said with a great yawn, "Dear me, what a great pity. All three of them were such clever children."

It was early winter by now, and each of the blue-eyed bees in the swarm was in the hexagonal home that he had made of wax, sleeping peacefully, dreaming of the spring to come.

3

THE RESTAURANT
OF MANY ORDERS

 T wo young gentlemen dressed just like British military men, with gleaming guns on their shoulders and two dogs like great white bears at their heels, were walking in the mountains where the leaves rustled dry underfoot. They were talking as they went.

"I must say, the country round here is really awful," said one. "Not a bird or beast in sight. I'm just dying to let fly—bang! bang!—at something. Anything, so long as it moves."

"Oh, what fun it would be to let a deer or something have two or three shots smack in his yellow

43

flank!" said the other. "I can just see him spinning round, then flopping down with a thud."

They were really very deep in the mountains. So deep, in fact, that the professional hunter who had come as their guide went astray and wandered off somewhere. Worse still, the forest was so frightening that the two dogs like white bears both got dizzy. They howled for a while, then foamed at the mouth, and died.

"Do you know, I've lost two thousand four hundred silver pieces with this dog," said one young gentleman, casually turning its eyelids back.

"*I've* lost two thousand eight hundred pieces," said the other, tilting his head ruefully to one side.

The first young gentleman went pale.

"I think I'll be getting back," he said, gazing into the other's face.

"Well, now," said the other, "I was just beginning to get cold, and hungry as well, so I think I'll be getting back, too."

"Then let's call it a day. What does it matter? On our way back we can call at yesterday's inn and buy a dozen pieces' worth of game birds to take home."

"They had hares too, didn't they? So it'll come to the same thing in the end. Well, why don't we go home, then?"

But the annoying thing was that by now they no longer had the faintest idea of the way back.

A sudden gust of wind sprang up; the grass stirred, the leaves rustled, and the trees creaked and groaned.

"I really am hungry!" said one. "I've had an awful empty feeling under my ribs for quite a while."

"So have I," said the other. "I don't feel like walking any farther."

"Oh, for something to eat!" said the first.

The pampas grass was rustling all about them as they talked.

Just then, one of them happened to look round, and what should he see standing there but a fine brick building. Over the entrance there was a notice that said, in large letters:

RESTAURANT WILDCAT HOUSE

"Look! This is just right," said one. "The place is civilized after all! Why don't we go in?"

"Funny," said the other, "in a place like this. But I expect we shall be able to get a meal, at any rate."

"Of course we shall, silly. What do you think the sign means?"

"Why don't we go in? I'm ready to collapse with hunger."

They stepped into the entrance hall. It was very fine, being done all over in white tiles. There was a glass door, with something written on it in gold letters.

PRAY COME IN. NO ONE NEED HAVE A MO-
MENT'S HESITATION.

They were terribly pleased.

"Just look at that!" said one of them. "Things always turn out right in the end. Everything's been going wrong all day, but look how lucky we are now. This place is a restaurant, but they feed you for nothing!"

"I must say, it seems like it," said the other. "That's what 'no one need have a moment's hesitation' means."

They pushed open the door and went through. On the other side was a corridor. Another notice in gold letters on the back of the glass door said:

PLUMP PARTIES AND YOUNG PARTIES
ESPECIALLY WELCOME.

They were both overjoyed at this.

"Look, we're especially welcome, it says," said one.

"Because we satisfy both conditions!" said the other.

They walked briskly along the corridor and came to another door, this time painted bright blue.

"What a strange place! I wonder why there are so many doors?"

"This is the Russian way of doing things, of course. It's always like this in cold places or in the mountains."

They were just going to open the door when they saw a notice in yellow letters above it:

WE HOPE YOU WILL APPRECIATE THAT THIS
IS A RESTAURANT OF MANY ORDERS.

"Awfully popular, this place. Just fancy, in the mountains like this."

"But of course. Why, even in the capital very few of the best restaurants are on the main streets, are they?"

As they were talking, they opened the door. A notice on the other side said:

THERE ARE RATHER A LOT OF ORDERS, BUT
WE HOPE YOU WILL BE PATIENT.

"Now just what would *that* mean?" said one young gentleman, screwing up his face.

"Mm—I expect it means that there are so many orders that it takes a long time before the food comes, so please forgive us. Something like that."

"I expect so. I want to get settled down in a room as soon as possible, don't you?"

"Yes, and get seated at a table."

But it was most frustrating—there was yet another door, and by the side of it hung a mirror, with a long-handled brush lying beneath it. On the door it said in red letters:

PATRONS ARE REQUESTED TO COMB THEIR
HAIR AND GET THE MUD OFF THEIR BOOTS
HERE.

"Very proper, too. And back in the hall just now
I was thinking this was just a place for the yokels."

"This place is very strict on etiquette. I'm sure they
often have very distinguished people here."

So they neatly combed their hair and got the mud
off their boots.

But no sooner had they put the brush back on its
shelf than it blurred and disappeared, and a sudden
gust of wind moaned through the room. They hud-
dled together in alarm and, flinging the door open,
went into the next room. Both of them were feeling
that unless they fortified themselves with something
warm to eat very soon, almost anything might
happen.

On the other side of the door there was another
unexpected sign:

PLEASE LEAVE YOUR GUNS AND CAR-
TRIDGES HERE.

Sure enough, there was a black gun rack right by
the door.

"Of course," said one young gentleman. "No one
ever ate with his gun."

"I must say, there must be awfully distinguished people here all the time," said the other.

They unshouldered their guns and unbuckled their belts and put them on the rack. Now there was another door, a black one, which said:

> BE KIND ENOUGH TO REMOVE YOUR HATS,
> OVERCOATS, AND BOOTS.

"What about it—do we take them off?"

"I suppose we'd better. They really must be *very* distinguished people they've got in the back somewhere."

They hung their hats and overcoats on the hooks, then took their boots off and padded on through the door. On the other side was the inscription:

> PLEASE REMOVE YOUR TIEPINS, CUFF LINKS,
> SPECTACLES, PURSES, AND EVERYTHING ELSE
> METAL, ESPECIALLY ANYTHING POINTED.

Right by the door a fine black-painted safe stood open and waiting. It even had a lock on it.

"Of course! It seems they use electricity somewhere in the cooking. So metal things are dangerous, especially pointed things. I expect that's what it means."

"I suppose so. I wonder if it means you pay the bill here on the way out, then?"

"It seems like it, doesn't it?"

"Yes, that must be it."

They took off their spectacles and their cuff links and so on, put everything in the safe, and clicked the lock shut.

A little further on, they came to another door, with a glass jar standing in front of it. On the door it said:

PLEASE SPREAD CREAM FROM THE JAR ALL OVER YOUR FACE, HANDS, AND FEET.

"Why should they want one to put cream on?"

"Well now, it's very cold outside, you know. If it's too warm inside one gets chapped skin, so this is to prevent it. I must say, they seem to be awfully distinguished people in the back. At this rate, we may soon be on speaking terms with the aristocracy!"

They rubbed cream from the jar on their faces and then on their hands. Then they took their socks off, and rubbed it on their feet as well. Even so, there was still some left, so they both ate some surreptitiously, pretending to be rubbing it on their faces all the while.

Then they opened the door in a great hurry—only to find a notice on the other side, which said:

DID YOU PUT ON PLENTY OF CREAM? ON YOUR EARS TOO?

There was another, smaller jar of cream here.

"Of course—I didn't do my ears. I might well have got them chapped. The proprietor of this place is really most thoughtful."

"Yes, he's got an eye for every little detail. Incidentally, I'd like something to eat, but it doesn't look very hopeful with these eternal corridors, does it?"

But the next door was already upon them, and there was written:

> THE MEAL WILL SOON BE READY. WE WON'T
> KEEP YOU AS MUCH AS FIFTEEN MINUTES.
> MAKE HASTE AND SHAKE SOME PERFUME
> OVER YOUR HEAD FROM THIS BOTTLE.

And there in front of the door stood a shining gilt perfume bottle.

They splashed perfume over their heads. Unfortunately, though, the perfume smelled dreadfully like vinegar.

"This perfume's awfully vinegary," said one young gentleman. "What's wrong with it, do you suppose?"

"They've made a mistake," the other said. "The maid must have had a cold or something and put the wrong stuff in."

They opened the door and went through. On the other side of the door was a notice in big letters that said:

> WHAT A WEARISOME LOT OF ORDERS, YOU

POOR THINGS. THERE ARE NO MORE, SO BE
GOOD ENOUGH TO TAKE SOME SALT FROM
THE POT AND RUB IT IN WELL ALL OVER YOU.

A fine blue china salt cellar was indeed standing
there, but this time both the young gentlemen were
quite horrified. They turned their cream-smeared faces
to look at one another.

"I don't like the look of this," said one.

"Nor do I," said the other.

" 'Lots of orders' means *they're* giving *us* orders."

"Yes—and it's my idea that 'restaurant' doesn't
mean a place for serving food, but a place for cooking people and serving *them*. And that m-m-means
that w-w-we . . ."

But he began to shake and tremble, and tremble
and shake, so that he couldn't go on.

"Then w-w-we . . . Oh *dear*!" And the other one,
too, began to quake and shiver, and shiver and quake,
so that he couldn't go on either.

"Let's get out!" Still shaking all over, one of the
young gentlemen pushed at the door behind him. But
strange to say, it refused to budge.

At the other end was another door with two big
holes and a silver knife and fork carved on it. It said:

SO NICE OF YOU TO COME. THAT WILL DO
VERY NICELY INDEED. NOW JUST POP INSIDE,
PLEASE.

What was worse, two blue eyeballs were ogling them through the keyhole.

"Oh dear!" cried one, quivering and trembling.

"Oh *dear!*" cried the other, trembling and quivering.

And they both burst into tears.

Just then, they heard voices talking furtively on the other side of the door.

"It's no good, they've realized. It doesn't look as if they're going to rub in the salt."

"What d'you expect? The way the boss put it was all wrong—'You poor things,' and the like—stupid, I call it."

"Who cares? Either way, *we* won't get as much as the bones even."

"How right you are. But if they won't come in here, it's our responsibility."

"Shall we call them? Yes, let's. Hey, gentlemen! This way, quickly. This way! The dishes are washed, and the vegetables nicely salted. All that's left is to arrange you nicely with the greens and put you on the snowy white dishes. This way now, quickly!"

The two young gentlemen were so distressed that their faces went all crumpled like pieces of wastepaper. They peered at each other and shook and shivered and wept silently.

There were chuckles on the other side of the door, then a voice shouted again, "This way, this way! If you cry like that, you know, you'll wash off all the cream you put on specially. (Yes, sir, coming, sir. We'll be bringing it in just a moment, sir.) Come on, this way now!"

"This way, quickly. The boss has his napkin tucked in and his knife in his hand and he's licking his lips, just waiting for you."

But the two young gentlemen just wept and wept and wept and wept.

Then, all of a sudden, they heard a "woof, woof" and a "grr!" behind them, and the two dogs like white bears came bursting through the door and into the room. The eyes behind the keyhole disappeared in a twinkling. Round and round the room the dogs rushed, snarling, then with another great "woof!" threw themselves at the next door. The door banged open, and they vanished inside as though swallowed up. From the pitch darkness beyond came a great miaowing and spitting and growling, then a rustling sound.

The room vanished in a puff of smoke, and the two young gentlemen found themselves standing in the grass, shivering and shaking in the cold. Their coats and boots, purses and tiepins were all there with them, hanging from the branches or lying among the roots of the trees. A gust of wind set the grass stirring, the leaves rustling, and the trees creaking and groaning.

The dogs came back, panting, and behind them someone called, "Gentlemen! Gentlemen!"

"Hey! Hey!" they shouted, suddenly recovering their spirits. "We're here. This way, quickly!"

The professional hunter in his straw cape came rustling towards them through the grass, and they really felt safe at last.

They ate the dumplings the guide had brought with him and returned to the capital, buying ten pieces' worth of game birds on their way.

But even back in the capital, and however long they soaked themselves in hot baths, their faces that had gone all crumpled like wastepaper would never go back to normal again.

4

THE UNGRATEFUL RAT

In the pitch-dark space in the ceiling of an old house there lived a rat.

One day, the rat was walking along the Underfloor Highway, peering about him as he went, when a weasel came dashing along from the other direction carrying a lot of something that looked good. When he saw the rat, he paused a moment and said in a rapid voice, "Hey, Rat! A lot of sugar balls have come through the hole in the closet at your place. Hurry and get some!"

His whiskers twitching with delight, the rat rushed straight off without so much as a thank you to the weasel. When he got to the place beneath the closet, however, he suddenly felt something pricking at his leg, and a tiny, shrill voice called, "Halt! Who goes there!"

The rat looked down in astonishment and found it was an ant. The ant soldiers had already set up a multiple barricade all around the sugar balls, and were brandishing their black battle-axes. Twenty or thirty of them were busily breaking up the sugar balls and dissolving them, getting them ready to take back to their nest. The rat started quaking with fright.

"Entry forbidden!" said a sergeant-major ant in a deep, resonant voice. "Off home with you! Be off now, quickly!"

The rat spun round and dashed straight home into the space in the ceiling, where he got into his nest and stayed still for some while. But he was very much put out. Nothing could be done about the ants—they were soldiers, after all, and powerful. But that meek fraud of a weasel—it was infuriating, the rat thought, that he should have run all the way to the closet and got turned back by the sergeant-major of the ants just because of what the weasel had told him. So the rat sneaked out of his nest again and went to the weasel's place at the back of the timber shed.

When he saw the rat, the weasel, who was just grinding some corn into powder with his teeth, said, "Well? Didn't you find any sugar balls?"

"Weasel—I think you're terrible, to deceive someone weak like me."

"Deceive? Nonsense. There were some there, all right."

"Oh, they were there, but the ants had already got at them."

"Ants? Had they, now. They're mighty quick, those ants."

"The ants took the lot. You should pay compensation for deceiving someone weak like me. Yes, compensation!"

"It's not my fault. You were a bit late, that's all."

"That's nothing to do with it. You shouldn't deceive someone weak like me. I want compensation!"

"You're a fine one, aren't you—throwing people's kindness in their faces. All right. If you like, I'll give you my own sugar balls."

"Compensation! Compensation!"

"Here, take them then! Take as many as you can carry and get out of here. I'm sick of you and your namby-pamby ways. Take all you can carry and get out!"

In a fine rage, the weasel flung out the sugar balls. The rat gathered up just as many as he could carry, then bowed.

"You!" shouted the weasel still more angrily. "Get

out! I don't want what you've left either. I'll give them to the maggots."

The rat dashed straight back to his nest in the ceiling, where he crunched his way through the sugar balls.

In this way, the rat gradually got himself disliked. In the end, there was no one who would have anything to do with him. So for want of anyone better, he began to associate with pillars, broken dustpans, buckets, brooms, and the like. He was especially friendly with a pillar.

One day, the pillar said to the rat, "Rat, it will soon be winter. We pillars will be creaking with the cold before long. You ought to get some good bedding together before it's too late. Luckily enough, just above my head there's a lot of bird feathers and other stuff that the sparrows brought in the spring. Why don't you fetch some down and take it home while the going's good? I may feel a bit cold round the head, but I'll manage somehow."

The rat thought it was a sensible idea, so that day, without delay, he set about carrying the bedding. Unfortunately, though, there was a steep slope on the way, and on the third journey the rat fell plump off it.

The pillar was startled. "Are you hurt, Rat? Are you hurt?" it called frantically, bending itself in the attempt to see.

After a while the rat got up, then, with his face

all twisted, he said, "Pillar, I'm shocked at you, letting this kind of thing happen to someone like me who's not strong."

The pillar, who felt terribly responsible for what had happened, apologized busily. "I'm sorry, Rat," he kept repeating. "Do forgive me!"

"It's not a matter of forgiving," said the rat, taking advantage of the situation. "If only you hadn't been so ready to give instructions, this wouldn't have happened to me. I want compensation. Come on, pay up!"

"But you know very well I can't. Please let me off."

"No, I don't like bullies, so you must pay me compensation. Come on now, pay up!"

Unable to do anything, the pillar wept bitterly. So the rat had no alternative but to return home to his nest. From that time on, the pillar was too scared to speak to the rat again.

It was one day some time after this that the dustpan gave the rat half a cake that someone had left. And it happened that the very next day the rat had an upset stomach. So, as usual, the rat demanded a full hundred times that the dustpan pay him compensation. The dustpan was so disgusted that he would have nothing more to do with the rat.

Later still, the bucket gave the rat a piece of washing soda and told him to wash his face with it each morning. The rat was very pleased and from the next morning on he used it every day for washing his face. But before long ten of his whiskers came out. So, sure enough, the rat went to the bucket and demanded a full hundred times that he be paid compensation. Unfortunately, however, the bucket had no whiskers, nor any other way of paying him back, so at a complete loss he just wept and apologized. And from then on he never said another word.

One by one, all the inhabitants of the kitchen in turn had the same trouble and learned to avoid the rat; in the end, they would turn away hastily at the mere sight of him.

There was, in fact, just one of them which had not yet had anything to do with the rat. It was a rattrap made of woven wire.

Rattraps ought, in theory, to be on the side of human beings, but this one had been feeling put out recently because of the advertisements in the papers with pictures showing a trap along with a cat, both labeled "disposable." Not that human beings had ever accorded the wire rattrap decent treatment, even before that. No, not once. And everybody avoided touching him as though he were something unclean. So the trap had less sympathy with human beings than with the rats. Most rats, even so, were too frightened to go anywhere near him. Every day he would call to them in a gentle voice, "Come on, Ratty, there's a mackerel head for dinner tonight. I'll hold the catch down firmly while you eat it. Don't be frightened. Come on, I'm not the kind to slam the entrance down behind you. I'm fed up with human beings, just like you."

But the rats all said, "Pooh, I'm not going to fall for that one," or "Really? I see . . . I'll have to speak to my father and my sons about it sometime," and made off as though there was all the time in the world.

Then the next morning a manservant with a bright red face would come to look at the trap and would say, "Nothing in it again. The rats know, that's the trouble. They learn about it at rat school. All the same, let's try just one more day." And he would change the bait in the trap.

That night as usual the trap called, "Come on, come on, tonight there's some nice soft fish cake. You can just have the bait, it's quite safe. Hurry up, now!"

The rat happened to be going past just then.

"Really, Trap?" he said. "Will you really just let me have the bait?"

"Well, hallo," said the trap. "You're a new rat around here, aren't you? Yes, of course—just the bait. Here, come in and help yourself."

The rat popped inside, gobbled up the fish cake, popped out again, and said, "That was very nice. Thanks."

"Was it? I'm glad. Come again tomorrow night."

The next morning the servant came to look and

said angrily, "Dammit! He's got away with the bait. This rat's a crafty one. Still, he went inside, that's something. There—there's a sardine for today." And he left half a sardine as bait.

The trap hooked onto the bait and waited eagerly for the rat to come along.

As soon as it was dark the rat appeared.

"Good evening. I've come as you asked me to," he said very patronizingly.

The trap was a little annoyed, but swallowed his pride and said simply, "Here, help yourself."

The rat popped inside, chewed down the sardine, and popped out again. Then he said haughtily, "I'll come and eat it again for you tomorrow."

"Umph," replied the trap.

When the servant came to look the next morning he got angrier still.

"Sly brute! But I don't see how he can just get away with the bait every night. If you ask me, this trap here has taken a bribe from the rat."

"I did nothing of the kind! What an insult!" shouted the trap, but of course the servant could not hear him. Once again he left some bait, this time a piece of rotten fish cake, fastened to the trap.

All day the trap fumed at the idea of being so un- justly suspected.

Night fell. The rat came out and said as though it was all a tremendous nuisance, "Ah me, it's not easy to come all the way here every day. And all for a fish head at the most. I've just about had enough. Still, I'm here now, so I might as well do him the favor of eating it. Good evening, Trap."

The trap was quivering so with rage that all he could get out was, "Help yourself."

The rat promptly popped inside, then saw that the fish cake was rotten and shouted, "Trap! This is going too far! This fish cake is rotten. How can you cheat a weak creature like me? I want compensation. Compensation!"

The trap was so angry that he could not stop his wire from rattling and quivering.

It was the quivering that did it.

With a snap and a swish, the catch that was fastened to the bait came free and the entrance to the trap fell shut. That really did it.

The rat went nearly mad.

"Terrible Trap! Liar! Cheat!" he cried, biting at the wire and dashing round and round in circles and stamping on the floor and shrieking and crying. It was a dreadful commotion. Even so, he hadn't the courage left this time to ask for compensation. The trap, too, what with pain and annoyance, could do nothing but rattle and shake and quiver. This went on all night until the morning.

The servant with the bright red face came to have a look and hopped for joy.

"Got him! Got him!" he cried. "Caught him at last! And a nasty-looking brute he is too. Right, come on out now! Out you come, my beauty!"

5

THE NIGHTHAWK
STAR

The nighthawk was really a very ugly bird. His face had reddish brown blotches as though someone had daubed it with bean paste, and his beak was flat, and his mouth stretched right round to his ears. His legs were quite unsteady, and he could barely walk even a couple of yards.

Things were so bad that the other birds had only to look at the nighthawk's face to take a dislike to him. Even the lark, who is not a very beautiful bird, considered himself far better than the nighthawk. If he met the nighthawk as he was setting out in the early evening, he would turn his head away with his eyes closed disdainfully, as though the nighthawk was really too distasteful for words. And the smaller birds who liked to chatter were always saying downright unpleasant things about him.

"Well! Here he comes again," they would say. "Just *look* at that, my dear! Did you ever see anything like it? It's really a disgrace to us birds!"

"Quite. Why, just look at the great mouth! I'm sure he's related to the frogs."

And so it went on. If only he had been a simple hawk instead of a nighthawk, his name alone would have been enough to send those half-baked little birds into hiding, all quivering and pale-faced, hunched up amidst the leaves of the trees. In fact, though, the nighthawk was not a brother of the hawk, nor even a relation. Surprising to say, he was elder brother to the beautiful kingfisher and to the jewel of birds, the hummingbird. The whole family was quite harmless to other birds. The hummingbird ate the honey from flowers, and the kingfisher ate fish, while the nighthawk lived by catching winged insects. The nighthawk had no sharp claws or sharp beak even, so that no one, not even the weakest bird, was afraid of him.

It may seem strange, indeed, that he should have been called "hawk" at all. In fact, there were two reasons. One was that the nighthawk's wings were exceptionally strong, so that when he soared through the air he looked just like a hawk. The other was his voice, which was piercing and also reminded people of the real hawk.

This bothered the real hawk very much, of course. If he so much as caught sight of the nighthawk, he would hunch up his shoulders and call out to him threateningly to get his name changed quickly.

Then, early one evening, the hawk actually visited the nighthawk at his home.

"Hey, are you in?" he called. "Haven't you changed your name yet? What a shameless bird you are! Don't you see that our natures are completely different? See how proudly I range the blue skies, whereas you never come out at all except on dark, cloudy days or at night. And take a look at my beak, too. You'd do well to compare it with your own!"

"I'm afraid I just can't do as you say, Hawk," the nighthawk replied. "I didn't choose my own name. It was given me by God."

"No, you're wrong. With *my* name, now, one might say it was given me by God, but yours is kind of borrowed—half from me and half from the night. Give it back!"

"But I *can't*, Hawk."

"Yes, you can! I'll tell you another name instead. Algernon. Algernon—right? Don't you think it's a nice name, now? When one changes one's name, of course, one has to have a ceremony to announce it to everybody. You understand? What you do is to go round to everybody's place wearing a sign saying 'Algernon' round your neck, and you bow and you say, 'From now on, I shall be known as Algernon.'"

"Oh, I could never do that!"

"Yes, you could. You've got to! If you don't do it by the morning of the day after tomorrow, I'll crush you to death. Remember, now! The day after tomorrow in the morning, I'll go round to all the other birds' houses and ask whether you've been there or not. If there's a single one that says you haven't, that'll be the end of you!"

"But how can you expect me to do such a thing? I'd rather die. So you might as well kill me right now."

"Come now, think about it more carefully later. Algernon's not half a bad name really." And the hawk spread wide his great wings and flew off home to his own nest.

The nighthawk sat perfectly still with his eyes shut, thinking. "Why on earth should everybody dislike me so much? Actually, I know quite well. It's because my face looks as though it's been daubed with bean paste and my mouth is slit from ear to ear. But in fact I've never done a bad thing all my life. Why, once I even rescued a baby white-eye that fell out of its nest, and took it back home. But the mother white-eye snatched it away from me as though she was recovering something from a thief. Then she laughed at me. And now—oh dear!—they want me to wear a sign round my neck saying 'Algernon'! Whatever shall I do?"

Night was already drawing in about him, and the nighthawk flew out from his nest. The clouds hung low, gleaming unpleasantly, and the nighthawk nearly brushed against them as he flew noiselessly about the sky.

Suddenly, his mouth opened wide and, setting his wings back straight, he shot down through the sky like an arrow. Insect after insect disappeared down his throat. Then, before you could tell whether he had actually touched the earth or not, he had swung up and was shooting skywards again.

The clouds were gray by now, and a forest fire glowed red on the hills in the distance.

Whenever the nighthawk decided to strike, he flew so fast that he seemed to cleave the sky in two. But tonight, among the insects he caught, there was a beetle that struggled dreadfully as it went down his throat. The nighthawk forced it down at once, but a kind of shudder went down his back as he did so.

Now the clouds were all black, except in the east, where the forest fire, red and frightening, was reflected on them. The nighthawk flew up to the sky again, feeling something heavy in his stomach.

Another beetle went into the nighthawk's maw,

but this one flapped about exactly as though it were scratching at his throat. The nighthawk got it down somehow, but even as he did so his heart gave a sudden lurch, and he started crying in a loud voice. Round and round and round the sky he circled, crying all the while.

"Oh dear," he said to himself, "here I am every night, killing beetles and all kinds of different insects. But now *I'm* going to be killed by Hawk, and there's only one of me. It's no wonder I feel so miserable. Oh, how wretched! I think I'll stop eating insects and starve to death. But then, I expect Hawk will kill me before that happens. No—I'll go away, far, far away into the sky before he can get me."

The flames of the forest fire were gradually spreading out like water, and the clouds were red as though they themselves were ablaze.

The nighthawk flew straight to the home of his younger brother, the kingfisher. Luckily enough, the beautiful kingfisher was still up, watching the distant forest fire.

"Good evening, Elder Brother," he said as he saw the nighthawk flying down towards him. "What brings you so unexpectedly?"

"It's just that I'm going far away, and I've come to see you before I go."

"But you mustn't, Elder Brother! Brother Hummingbird lives far away, and I shall be left all alone!"

"I'm afraid it can't be helped. Please don't say any more today. And you—please be sure not to catch any more fish than is absolutely necessary. Please. Goodbye."

"What's happened, Elder Brother? Here—don't go just yet!"

"No. It won't make any difference, however long I stay. Give Hummingbird my love when you see him. Goodbye. We shall never meet again. Goodbye."

And he went home weeping. The brief summer night was already giving way to the dawn.

The leaves of the ferns swayed green and gold, drinking in the morning mist. The nighthawk cried out loud and harsh. Then he made his nest neat and tidy, combed every bit of feather and down on his body into place, and set off from his nest again.

The mist cleared, and as it did so the sun climbed from the east. It was so dazzling that the nighthawk wavered for a moment, but he persevered and flew straight ahead in the direction of the sun.

"Sun, Sun," he called. "Won't you take me up with you? I'll gladly die in your fire if need be. My body may be ugly, yet it will surely give out a tiny light as it burns. Won't you take me up with you?"

But though he flew and flew, the sun grew no closer. In fact, it seemed to grow smaller and more distant still.

"Nighthawk, eh?" said the sun. "Why yes, I suppose you do have a hard time. Why don't you fly up into the sky tonight and ask the stars instead? You're really a bird of the night, you see."

The nighthawk gave what was meant to be a bow, but suddenly lost his balance and ended by falling down, down into the grass on the plain below.

For a while, everything was a dream. It seemed to the nighthawk that he was climbing up amidst the red and yellow stars, or that he was being swept away and away by the wind, or that the hawk had come and was crushing him in his claws.

Then something cold fell on his face, and he opened his eyes. The dew was dripping from a stem of young pampas grass. It was quite dark, and the deep indigo sky was covered all over with twinkling stars. The nighthawk flew up into the sky. The forest fire was gleaming red again tonight, and the nighthawk as he flew about found himself between the faint glow from the fire and the cold light of the stars above. Once more he flew round the sky, then suddenly made up his mind and started flying straight upward, towards the constellation of Orion in the western sky.

"Oh Stars!" he called as he went. "Bluish White Stars of the west! Won't you take me up with you? If need be, I'll willingly die in your fires."

But Orion was too busy singing his brave songs to pay the slightest heed to anything as insignificant as the nighthawk. Unsteadily and close to tears, the nighthawk came down until he finally reached a resting place. Once more he flew round the sky. Then off he went straight upward again, this time towards the Great Dog in the south.

"Oh Stars!" he cried as he went. "Blue Stars of the south! Won't you take me up with you? I'll gladly die in your fires if need be."

"Foolish talk!" said the Great Dog, busily winking blue and purple and yellow. "Whoever do you think you are? A mere bird—that's all. Why, to reach here with your wings would take hundreds and thousands and millions of billions of years!" And the Great Dog turned away again.

Disheartened, the nighthawk wavered back down to earth. He flew around the sky twice. Then again he summoned up his resolve and flew straight up in the direction of the Great Bear in the north.

"Oh Blue Stars of the north!" he cried as he went. "Won't you take me up with you?"

"Now, you mustn't say things you shouldn't," said the Great Bear softly. "Go and cool yourself off a little. At times like this, it's best to dive into a sea with icebergs, but if there's no sea handy, a cup of water with some ice in it will do nicely."

The nighthawk zigzagged dejectedly down to earth again. He flew around the sky four more times. Then he called out once more, to the Eagle, which had just risen on the opposite bank of the Milky Way.

"Oh White Stars of the east! Won't you take me up with you? I'll happily die in your fires if need be."

"Dear me, no. Quite out of the question!" said the Eagle pompously. "One must have the proper social status in order to become a star. And it takes a great deal of money, too."

All his remaining strength left the nighthawk. He folded in his wings and plummeted down towards the earth. But then, just when his weak legs were only inches from the ground, the nighthawk quite suddenly began to shoot upwards again like a rocket. Up he went, and when he came to the middle regions of the sky, he shook his body and ruffled up his feathers just as an eagle does before it attacks a bear.

He called and called again in a harsh, piercing voice. It was the voice of a hawk, and all the other birds who were asleep on the plains and in the woods below awoke and trembled as they looked up wonderingly at the starry sky.

The nighthawk climbed straight up and up, ever farther up into the sky. Now the flames of the forest fire below were no bigger than a burning cigarette end, yet still he climbed, up and up. His breath froze white on his breast with the cold, and the air grew thinner, so that he had to move his wings more and more frantically to keep going.

Yet the stars did not change their size. The

nighthawk wheezed at each breath like a pair of bellows. The cold and the frost pierced him like swords. In the end, his wings went completely numb and useless. Then, with tearful eyes, he gazed once more up into the sky—and that was the last of the nighthawk. No longer did he know whether he was falling or climbing, whether he was facing upward or downward. But his heart was at peace now, and his great, bloodied beak, though a little twisted, was surely smiling a little.

A while later, the nighthawk opened his eyes quite clearly, and saw that his own body was glowing gently with a beautiful blue light like burning phosphorous.

Next to him was Cassiopeia. The bluish white light of the Milky Way lay just at his back.

And the nighthawk star went on burning. It burned forever and forever. It is still burning to this day.

6

WILDCAT AND THE ACORNS

One Saturday evening, a most peculiar postcard arrived at Ichiro's house. This is what it said:

September 19

Mr. Ichiro Kaneta:
Pleased to know as how you're well. Tomorrow I've got a difficult case to judge, so please come. Please don't bring no firearms.

Yours respectfully,
Wildcat

That was all. The writing was terrible, and the ink so blobby it nearly stuck to the fingers. But Ichiro was beside himself with joy. He put the card in his satchel when no one was looking and took it to school, and all day long he was bouncing up and down with delight.

Even after he'd crept into bed that night, he still kept imagining Wildcat's face with its cat's grin, and the scene at tomorrow's trial, and so many other things that he couldn't sleep until quite late.

When he awoke, though, it was already broad daylight. He went outside, and there were the hills lined up beneath a bright blue sky, rising as fresh and clean as though they'd just been made. He hurried through his breakfast and set off alone up the path by the stream in the valley. There was a fresh morning breeze, and at each puff the chestnut trees showered their nuts in all directions. Ichiro looked up at them.

"Chestnut Trees, Chestnut Trees," he called. "Did Wildcat pass this way?"

And the chestnut trees paused a while in their rustling and replied, "Wildcat? Yes, he rushed past in a carriage early this morning, going to the east."

"The east? That's the direction I'm going. How strange! At any rate, I'll keep on this way and see. Thank you, Chestnut Trees."

The chestnut trees made no answer, but went on

scattering their nuts in all directions. So Ichiro went a little farther, and came to the Flute Falls. They were called the Flute Falls because there was a small hole about halfway up a pure white cliff, through which the water spurted, whistling like a flute before turning into a waterfall and dropping with a roar into the valley below. Facing the waterfall, Ichiro shouted up at it.

"Hello there, Flute Falls! Did Wildcat pass this way?"

"Wildcat?" replied the waterfall in a high, whistly voice. "Yes, he rushed past in a carriage a while ago, going to the west."

"The west?" said Ichiro. "That's the way my home is. How strange! Anyway, I'll go a bit farther and see. Thank you, Waterfall."

But the waterfall was already whistling to itself as it always did. So Ichiro went a little farther and came to a beech tree. Under the tree, a crowd of white mushrooms were playing together in a strange kind of orchestra, tiddley-tum-tum, tiddley-tum-tum. Ichiro bent down towards them.

"Hello, Mushrooms," he said. "Did Wildcat pass this way?"

"Wildcat?" replied the mushrooms. "Yes, he rushed past in a carriage early this morning, going to the south."

"That's strange," said Ichiro, racking his brains.

"That's in those mountains over there. Anyway, I'll go a bit farther and see. Thank you, Mushrooms."

But the mushrooms were already busy again, playing their strange music, tiddley-tum-tum, tiddley-tum-tum. . . .

Ichiro was walking on, when he noticed a squirrel hopping about in the branches of a walnut tree.

"You, Squirrel!" called Ichiro, beckoning to him to stop. "Did Wildcat pass this way?"

"Wildcat?" said the squirrel, shading his eyes with a paw as he peered down at Ichiro. "Yes, he rushed past this morning in a carriage while it was still dark, going to the south."

"The south?" said Ichiro. "That's strange—that's twice I've been told that. Ah well, I'll go a bit farther and see. Thank you, Squirrel."

But the squirrel had gone. All he could see was the topmost branches of the walnut tree swaying a little, and the leaves of the neighboring beech tree flashing for a moment in the sun.

A little farther on and the path along the stream grew narrower, then disappeared altogether. There was a small new path, however, leading up towards the dark wood to the south of the stream, so Ichiro set off up it. The branches of the trees were heavy and so densely growing that not the tiniest patch of blue sky was to be seen. The path became steeper and steeper. Ichiro's face turned bright red, and the sweat fell in great drops. But then, quite suddenly, he came out into the light. He had reached a beautiful golden meadow. The grass rustled in the breeze, and all around stood fine, olive-colored trees.

There, in the middle of the meadow, a most odd-looking little man was watching Ichiro. His back was bent, and in his hand he held a leather whip. Ichiro slowly went nearer to him, then stopped in astonishment. The little man was one-eyed, and his blind eye, which was white, was moving nervously all the time. His legs were very bandy, like a goat's and—most peculiar of all—his feet were shaped like spades.

"Do you happen to know Wildcat?" Ichiro asked, trying not to show his nervousness. The little man looked at Ichiro with his one eye, and his mouth twisted into a leer.

"Mr. Wildcat will be back in just a moment," he said. "You'll be Ichiro, I suppose?"

Ichiro started back in astonishment.

"Yes, I'm Ichiro," he replied. "But how did you know?"

The strange little man gave an even broader leer.

"Then you got the postcard?" he asked.

"Yes, that's why I came," Ichiro said.

"Terribly bad style, wasn't it?" asked the little man, looking gloomily down at the ground. Ichiro felt sorry for him.

"No," he said. "It seemed very good to me."

The little man gasped for joy and blushed to the tips of his ears. He pulled his coat open at the neck to cool himself, and asked, "Was the writing very good too?"

Ichiro couldn't help smiling.

"Very good," he said. "I doubt if even a fifth grader could write that well."

The little man suddenly looked depressed again.

"When you say fifth grader, you mean at primary school, I suppose?" His voice was so listless and pathetic that Ichiro was alarmed.

"Oh, no," he said hastily, "at university."

The little man cheered up again and grinned so broadly that his face seemed to be all mouth.

"I wrote that postcard," he shouted.

"Just who are you, then?" asked Ichiro, trying not to smile.

"I am Mr. Wildcat's coachman!" he replied.

A sudden gust of wind rippled over the grass, and the coachman gave a deep bow. Puzzled, Ichiro turned round, and there was Wildcat, standing behind him. He wore a fine coat of yellow brocade, and his green eyes as he stared at Ichiro were perfectly round. Ichiro barely had time to note that his ears were pointed and stuck up just like an ordinary cat's, when Wildcat gave a stiff little bow.

"Oh, good morning," said Ichiro politely, bowing in return. "Thank you for the postcard."

"Good morning," said Wildcat, pulling his whiskers out stiff and sticking out his chest. "I'm pleased to see you. The fact is, a most troublesome dispute arose the day before yesterday, and I don't quite know how to judge it, so I thought I might ask your opinion. But anyhow, make yourself at home, won't you? The acorns should be here any moment now. Really, you know, I have a lot of trouble with this trial every year."

He took a cigarette case from inside his coat, and put a cigarette in his mouth.

"Won't you have one?" he asked, and offered the case to Ichiro.

"Oh, no thank you," said Ichiro, startled.

"Ho, ho! Of course, you're still young," said Wildcat with a lordly kind of laugh. He struck a match and, screwing up his face self-consciously, puffed out a cloud of blue smoke. His coachman, who was standing by stiffly awaiting orders, seemed to be dying for a cigarette himself, for big tears were rolling down his face.

Just then, Ichiro heard a tiny crackling sound at his feet, like salt being put on the fire. He bent down in surprise to look and saw that the ground was covered with little round gold things, all twinkling away in the grass. He looked closer and found that they were acorns—there must have been over three hundred of them—all wearing red trousers and all chattering away about something at the top of their voices.

"Here they come! Just like a lot of ants," said Wildcat, throwing away his cigarette. Hurriedly he gave orders to the coachman. "You there, ring the bell," he said. "And cut the grass just there, where it's sunny."

The coachman took a big sickle from his side and feverishly swished down the grass in front of Wildcat. Immediately, the acorns came rushing out from the grass on all sides, glittering in the sun as they came, and began to chatter and clamor.

The coachman rang his bell. Clang, clang! it went. Clang, clang! the sound echoed through the woods, and the golden acorns became a little quieter. Unnoticed by Ichiro, Wildcat had put on a long black satin gown and was now sitting looking important in front of the acorns. It reminded Ichiro of pictures he had seen of crowds of tiny worshipers before a great, bronze idol.

Swish, crack! Swish, crack! went the coachman with his whip. The sky was blue and cloudless, and the acorns sparkled most beautifully.

"Don't you know this is the third day this case has been going on?" Wildcat began. "Now, why don't you call it off and make up with each other?"

His voice was a little worried, but he forced himself to sound important. No sooner had he spoken, however, than the acorns set up a commotion.

"No, it won't do! Whatever you say, the one with the most pointed head is best. And it's me who's the most pointed."

"No, you're wrong, the roundest one's best, I'm the roundest!"

"It's size, I tell you! The biggest. I'm the biggest, so I'm the best!"

"You're wrong there! I'm much bigger. Don't you remember the judge said so yesterday?"

"You're all wrong! It's the one who's the tallest. The tallest one, I tell you!"

"No, it's the one who's best at pushing and shoving. That's what settles it!"

The acorns were chattering so noisily that in the end one had absolutely no idea what it was all about. It was like stirring up a hornet's nest.

"That's enough," Wildcat bawled. "Where do you think you are! Silence! Silence!"

Swish, crack! went the coachman's whip, and at last the acorns were still.

"Don't you know this is the third day this trial has been going on?" demanded Wildcat, twisting his whiskers till they stood on end. "How about calling it off now and making things up?"

"No, no, it's no good. Whatever you say, the one with the most pointed head's best."

"No, you're wrong. The roundest one's best!"

"No, he's not, it's the biggest!"

Chatter, chatter, chatter again, till you had no idea what it was all about.

"Enough! Where do you think you are!" Wildcat shouted. "Silence! Silence!"

Swish, crack! went the coachman's whip again. Wildcat twisted his whiskers till they stood on end, then started again.

"Don't you know this is the third day this case has been going on? Why don't you call it off and make things up!"

"No, no, it's no good! The one with the most pointed head . . ." Chatter, chatter, chatter . . .

"That's enough!" Wildcat shouted again. "Where do you think you are! Silence! Silence!"

Again the coachman's whip went swish, crack! and the acorns fell silent once more.

"You see what it's like," whispered Wildcat to Ichiro. "What do you think I ought to do?"

Ichiro smiled. "Well, then, how about giving a verdict like this?" he said. "Tell them that the best is the one who's most stupid, most ridiculous, and most good-for-nothing. I heard that in a sermon, you know."

Wildcat nodded wisely and prepared to give his verdict. With an enormous air of importance, he pulled open his satin gown at the neck so that the yellow brocade coat showed a little. Then he spoke.

"Right! Be quiet now! Here is my verdict. The best of you is the one who is least important, most foolish, most ridiculous, absolutely good-for-nothing, and completely crackbrained!"

A hush fell over the acorns, such a complete hush that you could have heard a pin drop.

Wildcat took off his black satin gown and, wiping the sweat from his forehead, took Ichiro's hand, while the coachman cracked his whip five or six times for sheer joy.

"I'm most obliged to you," said Wildcat to Ichiro. "I must say, you've taken a most awkward case off my hands in not so much as a minute and a half. I do hope you'll act as honorary judge for my court in the future. If ever I send you a postcard from now on, please come, won't you? I'll see you're suitably rewarded every time."

"Of course I'll come," said Ichiro. "But I don't want any reward."

"Oh, no," objected Wildcat. "You must accept a reward. It's a matter of honor for me, you see. And from now on, I'll address the postcard 'Ichiro Kaneta, Esq.,' and call this 'The Court'—is that all right?"

"That's fine," said Ichiro.

Wildcat was silent for a moment, twirling his whiskers as though there was something more he wanted to say. Then he seemed to take courage and went on, "And about the wording of the card—how would it be if I put it like this: 'Pertaining to certain business in hand, your presence in court is formally requested'?"

Ichiro smiled. "It seems a little funny to me, somehow," he said. "Perhaps you'd better leave that bit out, at any rate."

Wildcat gazed crestfallen at the ground, still twiddling his whiskers as though regretting that he hadn't put it better. Finally, with a sigh, he went on, "Well, then, we'll leave it as it stands. Oh yes—about your reward for today. Which do you prefer, a pint of gold acorns or a salted salmon head?"

"The gold acorns, please," replied Ichiro.

Wildcat straightway turned to the coachman, as if relieved that it hadn't been the salmon head.

"Get a pint of gold acorns," he said, speaking fast. "If there aren't enough, you can put in some gold-plated ones. And be quick!"

The coachman began to scoop the acorns into a measure. When he had finished, he gave a shout. "Just a pint," he said.

Wildcat's brocade coat flapped in the breeze. He stretched, closed his eyes, and smothered a yawn.

"Right!" he said. "Now hurry and get the coach ready."

A carriage made of a great white mushroom appeared, drawn by a horse of a most peculiar shape and gray in color, just like a rat. Wildcat turned to Ichiro.

"Well, now we'll see you home," he said.

They got into the carriage, and the coachman put the measure full of acorns in beside them. Swish, crack! and off they went. The meadow was left behind, and trees and bushes swayed by in a bluish haze. Ichiro's eyes were fixed on his gold acorns, and Wildcat was gazing quite innocently into the distance.

But as the carriage went on, the acorns lost their glitter, and when—in no time, it seemed—the carriage came to a halt, they were just the plain, ordinary, brown kind. Wildcat's yellow brocade coat, and the coachman, and the mushroom carriage—all had vanished together, and Ichiro was left standing before his own home, the measure of acorns in his hand.

From that time on, there were no more postcards signed "Yours respectfully, Wildcat." Ichiro sometimes wonders about it. Perhaps he ought to have let Wildcat write "Your presence is formally requested" after all?

7

THE FIRST
DEER DANCE

From a gap in the ragged, gleaming clouds to the west, the setting sun slanted down red on the mossy plain, and the swaying fronds of pampas grass shone like white fire. I was tired, and lay down to sleep. Gradually, the rustling of the breeze began to sound to my ears like human speech, and before long it was telling me the true meaning of the Deer Dance that the countryfolk still dance in the hills and on the plain of Kitakami.

Long ago, in the days when the area was still

covered all over with tall grass and black forests, Kaju, together with his grandfather and the others, came to live there from somewhere east of the river Kitakami. They settled there, cleared the land, and began growing millet.

One day, Kaju fell out of a chestnut tree and hurt his knee a little. At such times, it was the local custom to go to the mountains to the west where there was a hot spring, build a hut there, and bathe in the spring until one was cured.

One fine morning, then, Kaju set out for the spring. With his rice, his bean paste, and his pot on his back, he walked slowly, limping slightly as he went, across the open country where the plumes of pampas grass were blowing silver.

On he went, over streams and across stony wastes, till the mountain range loomed large and clear and he could pick out each single tree on the mountains like the pins on a pincushion. By now the sun was far gone in the west and glittered with a greenish tinge just above the tops of a stand of a dozen alder trees.

Kaju set the load from his back down on the grass, took out some horse-chestnut and millet dumplings, and began to eat. The pampas grass spread away from him in clump after clump—so many clumps that it seemed to ripple in shining white waves all over the plain. As he ate his dumplings, Kaju thought to himself what a fine sight the trunks of the alder trees made, rising perfectly straight out of the pampas grass.

But he had walked so energetically that he was almost too tired to eat. He was soon full, and in the end, despite himself, he had to leave a piece of dumpling about the size of a horse-chestnut burr.

"I'll leave 'er for the deer," he said to himself. "Deer, do 'ee come and eat!" And he set it down by a small white flower that grew at his feet. Then he shouldered his pack once more and slowly, quite slowly, set off again.

But he had only gone a short way when he realized that he had left his cotton towel at the place where he had rested, so he turned back again in a hurry. He could still see the stand of alder trees quite clearly, so to go back was really not much trouble. Yet before he reached the place, he suddenly stopped quite still, sensing beyond all doubt that the deer were already there.

And there, indeed, they were—at least five or six, walking towards something, with their moist noses stretched out far in front of them. Kaju tiptoed softly over the moss towards them, taking care not to brush against the pampas grass.

No mistake about it, the deer had come for the dumpling he had left. "Hah, deer bain't wasting no time," he muttered to himself with a smile and, bending down low, crept slowly in their direction.

He peeped out from behind a clump of pampas

grass, then drew back in surprise. Six deer were walking round and round in a ring on the stretch of grassy turf. Hardly daring to breathe, Kaju peered out at them from between the pampas stems.

The sun had touched the summit of one of the alder trees, and its topmost branches shone with a strange green light, so that it looked for all the world like some green living creature standing stock still, gazing down at the deer. Each plume of pampas grass shone separate and silver, and the deer's coats seemed even shinier and sleeker than usual. Delighted, Kaju gently lowered himself onto one knee and concentrated on watching the deer.

They were going round and round in a wide circle, and he soon noticed that every one of them seemed intent on something that lay in the center of the ring. He was sure of it, because their heads and ears and their eyes were all pointing in that direction. What was more, from time to time one or the other of them would break the circle and stagger a few paces inwards as though drawn towards the center.

In the center of the ring, of course, was the horsechestnut dumpling that Kaju had left there a while ago. The thing that was bothering the deer so much, though, was not the dumpling, it seemed, but Kaju's white cotton towel, which lay in a curve where it had fallen on the ground. Bending his bad leg gently with one hand, Kaju sat himself neatly on his heels on the moss in order to watch.

Gradually the deer's circling slowed down. Now they trotted gently, every so often breaking out of the ring and putting one foreleg forward towards the center as though about to break into a run, then just as soon drawing back again and trotting on once more. Their hooves thudded pleasantly on the dark soil of the plain. Finally, they stopped going round and round altogether and came and stood in a group between Kaju and the towel.

Without warning, Kaju's ears began to ring and his body began to shake: the same feeling that the deer were feeling, a feeling as of grass swaying in the breeze, was coming to him in waves. The next moment, he really doubted his own ears, for now he could actually hear the deer talking.

"Shall I go for to look, then?" one was saying.

"Naw, 'er be dangerous. Better watch 'er a bit longer."

"Can't get caught with no trick like old Fox played on us. 'Er be only a dumpling, when all's said and done."

"Right, right. Only too right."

So went the deer's talk.

" 'Er may be alive."

"Aye, 'er be summat like a living crittur, indeed."

In the end one of them seemed to make up his

mind. He straightened his back, left the ring, and went in towards the center. All the other deer stopped to watch.

The deer who had gone forward edged towards the towel inch by inch with his neck stretched out just as far as it would go and his legs all bunched up beneath him. Then, quite suddenly, he shot up in the air and came darting back like an arrow. The other five deer scattered in all four directions, but the first deer stopped dead when he got back to where he had started, so they calmed down and, reluctantly returning, gathered in front of him.

"How were it? What do 'er be? That long white thing?"

"'Er do have wrinkles all the way down 'er."

"Then 'er bain't a living crittur. 'Er be a toadstool or something after all! Poisonous too, I don't doubt."

"Naw, 'er bain't no toadstool. 'Er be a living thing all right."

"Be 'er, now! Alive and lots of wrinkles too—'er be getting on in years, then."

"Aye, that sentry guarding the dumpling be a very *elderly* sentry. Oh, ho, ho, ho, ho!"

"Eh, he, he, he, he! A blue and white sentry!"

"Oh, ho, ho, ho, ho! Private Blue-'n-White."

"Shall I go for to look now?"

"Do 'ee go, now. 'Er be safe enough."

"'Er won't bite, now?"

"Naw, 'er be safe, I'd say."

So another deer crept slowly forward. The five who stayed behind nodded their heads approvingly as they watched.

The deer who had gone forward seemed scared to death. Time and time again he bunched his four legs up and arched his back ready for flight, only to stretch them out gingerly and creep forward again the next moment.

At last he reached a spot only a step away from the towel. He stretched his neck out just as far as it would go and went sniff, sniff, at the towel, then suddenly leaped up in the air and came running back. They all started and began to run off, but the first deer stopped dead as soon as he got back, so they took courage and gathered their faces close about his head.

"How were 'er? Why did 'ee run away?"

"But I thought 'er were going to bite I!"

"What *can* 'er be, now?"

"No telling. What be sure is that 'er be white and blue, in patches, like."

"How do 'er smell? Eh, the smell?"

"'Er do smell like willow leaves."

"Do 'er breathe?"

"Now, I didn't rightly notice that."

"Shall I go now?"

"Aye, do 'ee go now."

The third deer crept slowly forward. Just then a slight breeze stirred the towel. He halted in his tracks in fright, and the others gave a violent start. After a while, though, he seemed to calm down, and crept forward again until at last he could stretch the tip of his nose out to the towel.

The five deer left behind were nodding at each other knowingly. But just then the deer out in front went quite stiff, shot up in the air, and came racing back.

"What did 'ee run away for?"

"Because I had a strange feeling, like."

"Be 'er breathing?"

"Well, I don't rightly think I heard 'er *breathing*. 'Er don't seem to have no mouth, either."

"Do 'er have a head?"

"I couldn't rightly tell about that, either."

"Then shall I go and see this time?"

The fourth deer went out. He was really just as scared as the rest. Even so, he went all the way up to the towel and, ever so boldly, pressed his nose right against it. Then he drew back in a hurry and came dashing back towards them like an arrow.

"Ah, 'er be soft."

"Like mud, would 'er be?"

"Naw."

"Like the fur on bean pods?"

"Mm—summat harder than that."

"What could 'er be, now?"

"Any rate, 'er be a living crittur."

" 'Ee think so, after all?"

"Aye, 'er be *sweaty*."

"I'm thinking I'll go and have a look."

The fifth deer in his turn crept forward slowly. This one seemed to be something of a joker, for he dangled his nose right over the towel, then gave his head a great jerk as much as to say, "This is very suspicious, now." The other five deer leaped about with amusement.

This encouraged the deer out in front, and he gave the towel a great lick. But then he, too, was suddenly seized with fright and came dashing back like the wind, with his mouth open and his tongue lolling out. The others were dreadfully alarmed.

"Were 'ee bitten, then? Did 'er hurt?"

But he just shivered and shivered.

"Has your tongue come loose, then?"

Still he shivered and shivered.

"Now, what be up with 'ee? Speak up, now!"

"Phew! Ah! My tongue be all numb, like!"

"What kind of taste do 'er have?"

"No taste."

"Would 'er be alive?"

"I don't rightly know. Do 'ee go and have a look now."

"Aye."

Slowly, the last deer went forward. The others all watched, nodding their heads with interest as he bent down and sniffed at it for a while. Then, quite suddenly, he picked it up in his mouth and came back with it as though there was nothing whatsoever to be afraid of any more. The other deer bounded up and down with delight.

"Well done! Well done! Once we've got *'er*, bain't nothing to be afeared of!"

"For sure, 'er be a great dried-up slug."

"Come on now, I'll sing, so do 'ee all dance around 'er."

The deer who had said this went into the middle of the group and began to sing, and the rest began to circle round and round the towel.

They ran and circled and danced, and again and again as they did so one or the other of them would dash forward like the wind and stab the towel with his antlers or trample it with his hooves. In no time, Kaju's poor towel was all muddy and holed. Then gradually the deer's circling began to slow down.

"Ah, *now* for the dumpling!"

"Ah, a boiled dumpling 'n all!"

"Ah, 'er be quite round!"

"Ah, yum yum!"

"Ah, wonderful!"

The deer split up and gathered in a ring about the horse-chestnut dumpling. Then they all ate one mouthful of it in turn, beginning with the deer who had gone up to the towel first. The sixth and last deer got a piece hardly bigger than a bean.

Then they formed a ring again and began to walk round and round and round in a circle. Kaju had been watching the deer so intently that he almost felt he himself was one of them. He was on the point of rushing out to join them, when he caught sight of his own great, clumsy hand. So he gave up the idea, and went on concentrating on breathing quietly.

Now the sun had reached the middle branches of the alder tree and was shining with a slightly yellowish light. The deer's dance grew slower and slower. They began nodding to each other busily, and soon drew themselves up in a line facing the sun, standing perfectly straight as though they were worshiping it. Kaju watched in a dream, forgetful of everything else. Suddenly, the deer at the right-hand end of the line began to sing in a high, thin voice.

> See the setting sun decline,
> Blazing out behind the leaves
> That delicately shine
> Green upon the alder tree.

Kaju shut his eyes and shivered all over at the sound of the voice, which was like a crystal flute.

Now the second deer from the right suddenly leaped up and, twisting his body to and fro, ran in and out between the others, bowing his head time and time again to the sun till finally he came back to his own place, stopped still, and began to sing.

> Now the sun's behind its back,
> See the leafy alder tree
> Like a mirror crack
> And shatter in a million lights.

Kaju caught his breath and himself bowed low to the sun in its glory, and to the alder tree. The third deer from the right began to sing now, bowing and raising his head busily all the while.

> Homeward though the sun may go,
> Down beyond the alder tree,
> See the grass aglow,
> Dazzling white across the plain.

It was true—the pampas grass was all ablaze, like a sea of white fire.

> Long and black the shadow lies
> On the shimmering pampas grass
> Where against the skies
> Straight and tall the alder grows.

Now the fifth deer hung his head low and started singing in a voice that was hardly more than a mutter.

> See, the sun is sinking low

In the shimmering pampas grass.
Ants now homeward go
Through the moss upon the plain.

Now all the deer were hanging their heads. But suddenly the sixth deer raised his head proudly and sang:

Shy white flower, content to pass
Your days unnoticed in the tall
And shimmering pampas grass—
You are dearest of them all!

Then all the deer together gave a short, sharp call like the cry of a flute, leaped up in the air, and began to dash round and round in a ring.

A cold wind came whistling from the north. The alder tree sparkled as though it really were a broken mirror. Its leaves actually seemed to tinkle as they brushed against each other, and the plumes of the pampas grass seemed to be whirling round and round with the deer.

By now Kaju had forgotten all about the difference between himself and the deer. "Hoh! Bravo, bravo!" he cried, and rushed out from behind the pampas grass.

For one moment the deer stopped stiff and straight in alarm, then the next instant they were fleeing like leaves before a gale. Their bodies bent forward in haste, breasting the waves of silver pampas grass and the shining sunset, they fled far, far into the distance, leaving the pampas grass where they had passed glittering on and on, like the wake of a boat left on a quiet lake.

Kaju smiled a rueful smile. Then he picked up his muddy, torn towel and set off walking towards the west.

And that was all, until I heard the story from the clear autumn breeze in the late sunlight that day on the mossy plain.

8

GORSH
THE CELLIST

Gorsh was the man who played the cello at the moving picture house in town. Unfortunately, he had a reputation for being none too good a player. "None too good," perhaps, was hardly the word, for if the truth be told, he was worse than any of his fellow musicians and was forever being bullied by the conductor for that reason.

One afternoon they were all sitting in a circle backstage rehearsing the Sixth Symphony, which they were soon to perform at the town's concert hall.

The trumpets were blaring for all they were worth.

The clarinets were tootling away in support.

The violins, too, were playing like fury.

Gorsh was scraping away with the rest of them, oblivious to all else, his lips pressed tight together and his eyes as big as saucers as he stared at the music in front of him.

All of a sudden the conductor clapped his hands together.

They all stopped playing instantly, and a complete hush fell over them.

"The cello was late!" shouted the conductor. "Tum-tiddy, tiddy-tee—once more from the bit that goes tum-tiddy, tiddy-tee. Right?" They all started again from a point just before where they had got to. With his face red and his forehead all sweaty, Gorsh managed somehow to get safely past the tricky bit. And he was playing the next bit with a feeling of relief when, once again, the conductor clapped his hands.

"Cello! You're off pitch! Whatever are we to do with you? You don't think I've got time to teach you the simple scale, do you?"

The others looked sorry for Gorsh and deliberately peered at their own scores or busily set about tuning their own instruments. Hastily, Gorsh tightened his strings.

"From the bar before the last place. Right!"

They all started again. Gorsh's mouth was twisted with the effort to play right. And this time they got quite a way without trouble. He was just feeling rather pleased with himself when the conductor scowled and clapped his hands together yet again. "Oh no—not again," thought Gorsh, with a leap of his heart. But this time, luckily, it was someone else. So Gorsh deliberately peered closely at his music, as the others had done for him just now, and did his best to look engrossed in something else.

"Well then, straight on to the next bit. Right!"

But Gorsh, with a smug feeling, had no sooner started playing when the conductor gave a great stamp with his foot and started shouting.

"It won't do. You're all at sixes and sevens. This part's the heart of the whole work, and see what a hash you're making of it. Gentlemen, we've got just ten days till the performance. We're professional musicians—how could we look people in the eyes if we let some bunch of second-rate scrapers and blowers outdo us? You, Gorsh. You're one of the chief troubles. You just don't have any *expression*. No anger, no joy—no feeling at all. And you don't keep in perfect time with the other instruments, either. You always drag along behind with your shoelaces dangling. It won't do—you must pull yourself together. It's not fair to the rest to let the illustrious name of the Venus Orchestra be dragged in the mud all because of one man. Well, then—that's enough rehearsal for today. Have a rest and be in the box at six sharp."

They all bowed, then put cigarettes in their mouths and struck matches or went outside somewhere.

With his cheap, boxlike cello held in his arms, Gorsh turned to face the wall. His mouth twisted and great tears rolled down his cheeks, but he soon pulled himself together and, all by himself, began to play again from the beginning, very softly, the part they had just done.

Late that evening, Gorsh arrived home carrying an enormous black object on his back. His home was really no more than a tumbledown old millhouse standing by the river on the outskirts of the town. He lived there all alone. His mornings he spent pruning the tomatoes in the small field surrounding the mill and picking grubs off the cabbages, but in the afternoon he always went out.

Gorsh went indoors and opened the black bundle. It was, of course, the ugly great cello he had been playing earlier that evening. He lowered it gently to the floor, then suddenly took a glass and gulped down some water out of a bucket.

Then he gave a shake of his head, sat down on a chair, and began to play the piece of music they had done that day, attacking his instrument with all the ferocity of a tiger.

Turning over the pages of the score, he played a while and thought, thought a while and played, then when he got to the end he started again from the beginning, rumbling his way through the same thing over and over again.

He went on long past midnight, till in the end he hardly knew whether it was himself playing or someone else. His expression was terrible, with bright red face and eyes all bloodshot, looking as though he might collapse at any moment.

Just then, though, somebody tapped three times on the door behind him.

"Is that you, Horsh?" Gorsh called as though half-asleep. However, it was not Horsh who pushed open the door and came walking in, but a large tortoiseshell cat that he had seen around several times before.

The cat was carrying, with enormous effort it seemed, a half-ripe tomato from Gorsh's field, which he set down in front of Gorsh.

"Oh, dear," he said "I'm tired. Carrying things is a terrible job."

"Whatever? . . . ." exclaimed Gorsh.

"A present for you," said the tortoiseshell cat. "Please eat it."

All the annoyance Gorsh had been damming up inside him since earlier that day came bursting out at once.

"Who told you to bring any tomato? Do you think I'd eat something brought by the likes of you in the first place? And that tomato, what's more, comes from my field. What do you think you're up to? Picking them before they ripen! I suppose it's you, then, who's been biting at the stalks of my tomatoes and scattering them all over the place? Get out of here! Damned cat!"

All this made the cat's shoulders droop and his eyes go narrow, but he forced a grin and said, "You shouldn't get so angry, sir, it's bad for your health. Why don't you play something instead? Schumann's 'Träumerei,' say. . . . I'll be your audience."

"That's enough impertinence! From a mere cat, indeed!"

Feeling furious, Gorsh spent a while thinking of the things he'd like to do to this nuisance of a cat.

"No, don't be shy, now," said the cat. "Please. You know, I can't get to sleep unless I hear you play something."

"That's enough of your cheek! Enough, I say! Enough!"

Gorsh had gone bright red and was shouting and stamping just as the conductor had done earlier that day. Suddenly, though, he changed his mind and said, "All right then, I'll play!" Ominously, he locked the door and shut all the windows, then got his cello out and turned off the light. When he did so, the light of the moon shone halfway into the room from outside.

"What d'you want me to play?"

". . . 'Träumerei.' Composed by Schumann," said the cat perfectly seriously, wiping his mouth as he spoke.

"Oh. 'Träumerei,' indeed. Would this be how it goes?"

Ominously again he tore his handkerchief into strips and stuffed up both his ears tightly. Then he stormed straight into a piece called "Tiger Hunt in India."

For a while, the cat listened with bowed head, but quite suddenly he blinked his eyes rapidly and made a leap for the door. His body collided with the door, which refused to open. This threw the cat into a great state of agitation, as though he had made some horrible mistake, and sparks crackled from his eyes and forehead. Next, sparks came from his whiskers and nose too, which tickled so that for a while he looked as though he was going to sneeze, but even so, he started trotting round as though to say "I've no time for this kind of thing." Gorsh was delighted at the effect he was producing, and began to play all the harder.

"Mr. Gorsh, that's enough, thank you," said the cat. "Quite enough. I beg you to stop. I promise I'll never tell you what to do again."

"Quiet! We're just getting to the bit where they catch the tiger."

By now the cat was leaping up and down in

distress, running round and round and rubbing against the walls, which gave off a green glow for a while where he had touched them. In the end, he was whirling round and round Gorsh like a merry-go-round.

Gorsh's own head began to spin a little, so he said, "All right then, I'll let you off now." And he stopped at last.

But now the cat looked quite unconcerned. "Mr. Gorsh, there's something funny about your playing tonight, isn't there?" he said.

Gorsh felt deeply aggrieved again, but he nonchalantly got out a cigarette and put it in his mouth, then took a match and said, "What about it? Are you sure there's nothing wrong with *you*? Let's have a look at your tongue."

Rather disdainfully the cat stuck out his long, pointed tongue.

"Ha-ha! Rather rough, I'm afraid," said the cellist and without warning struck the match on the cat's tongue and lit his cigarette with it. To say the cat was startled would be putting it too mildly: waving his tongue about like a windmill, he rushed to the door and dashed his head against it, staggered away, then went back and banged it again, staggered, went back again, banged it once more and staggered, trying desperately to find some way of escape.

For a while Gorsh watched in amusement, then

he said, "I'll let you out. So mind you don't come again. Stupid!"

He opened the door, and the cat streaked off like lightning through the pampas grass. Gorsh smiled a little as he watched him go, then went to bed and slept soundly as though a load had been lifted from his mind.

The next evening, too, Gorsh came home carrying on his back the black bundle containing his cello. Then he gulped down a great deal of water and began to scrub away at his cello exactly as on the previous evening. Soon twelve o'clock came, then one, then two, and still Gorsh went on. And he was still booming away, scarcely aware of the time or even of the fact that he was playing, when he heard someone tapping on the other side of the ceiling.

"What! . . . Haven't you had enough yet, cat?" he shouted, whereupon a scuffling sound came from a hole in the ceiling and a gray bird came down through it. It landed on the floor, and he found it was a cuckoo.

"So now I have birds, too," said Gorsh. "What do *you* want?"

"I want to learn music," said the cuckoo quite seriously.

"Music, eh?" said Gorsh with a smile. "But all you can sing is 'Cuckoo, cuckoo,' surely?"

"Yes," said the cuckoo very earnestly, "That's right. But that's very difficult, you see."

"Difficult, indeed! The only thing that's a trouble for cuckoos is having to sing such a lot. There's nothing difficult about the actual notes, is there?"

"No, actually that's just why it's so hard. For example, if I sing like this, 'Cuckoo,' and then like this, 'Cuckoo,' you can tell they're different just by listening, can't you?"

"There's no difference, if you ask me."

"That means you can't distinguish properly. As far as we cuckoos are concerned, you could sing ten thousand 'cuckoos' and they'd all be different."

"As you like. If you're so good at it, why do you have to come to me?"

"But you see, I want to learn the scale correctly."

"What could you care about the scale?"

"Oh, but one needs it if one's going abroad."

"What could *you* care about going abroad?"

"Sir—please teach me the scale. I'll sing it with you as you play."

"Oh, dear! Look. I'll play it just three times, then when I've finished you must clear off home."

Gorsh took up his cello, scraped at the strings as he tuned them, then played, "Do, re, mi, fa, so, la, ti, do."

But the cuckoo fluttered his wings agitatedly.

"No, no. That's not how it should go."

"There's no pleasing you. You try it, then."

"This is how it goes." The cuckoo bent forward slightly, braced himself, and emitted a single "Cuckoo."

"Well! Do you call that a scale? If it is, then the ordinary scale and the Sixth Symphony are all the same to you cuckoos."

"Oh no, they're quite different."

"How?"

"One of the difficult things is when you get a lot of them in succession."

"You mean like this, I suppose?" Gorsh took up his cello again and started to play in succession, "Cuckoo, cuckoo, cuckoo."

This delighted the cuckoo so much that halfway he began to bawl "Cuckoo, cuckoo, cuckoo" in time with Gorsh. On and on he went, twisting his body for all he was worth.

In time Gorsh's hand began to hurt, so he stopped.

"Here," he said, "that's about enough, isn't it?"

But the cuckoo just narrowed his eyes regretfully and went on singing for a while, till finally he went "Cuckoo, cuck—cuck—cuck—cu—" and stopped.

By now Gorsh was quite angry.

"Here, bird—if you've finished, be off with you now."

"Oh, please. Won't you play it once more? Yours

seems good enough, but there's something not quite right."

"What? I'm not supposed to be learning from you. Be off with you, now."

"Please, just once more. Please . . ." said the cuckoo, bobbing his head deferentially.

"Well, then, just this once." Gorsh got his bow ready.

The cuckoo gave a single "Cuck!" then said, "As long as possible if you don't mind." He gave another bow.

"Heaven help us," said Gorsh and with a wry smile began to play. Again the cuckoo got quite wrapped up in things and sang for all he was worth, twisting his body to and fro.

"Cuckoo, cuckoo, cuckoo."

At first Gorsh felt very irritated, but as he played on he gradually began to have an odd feeling that it was the cuckoo, somehow, who was really hitting the notes of the scale. In fact, the more he played the more he had the feeling that the cuckoo was better than he was.

"Hah! If I go on fooling around like this I shall end up by becoming a bird myself," he said, and quite abruptly stopped playing.

The cuckoo reeled as though someone had dealt him a hefty blow on the head, then just as he had done before sang, "Cuckoo, cuckoo, cuck—cuck—cuck—" and stopped.

"Why did you stop?" he said, looking at Gorsh resentfully. "If you were a cuckoo, even the least self-respecting one, you'd have gone on at the top of your voice till your throat was too sore to go on."

"Why, you cheeky. . . . Do you think I can go on fooling around like this forever? Come on, now, get out. Look—don't you see it's nearly dawn?" He pointed to the window.

The eastern sky was turning faintly silver where black clouds were scudding across it towards the north.

"Then won't you go on until the sun rises? Just once more. It's only a little longer."

Again the cuckoo bowed his head.

"That's enough! You seem to think you can get away with anything. Stupid bird, if you don't get out I'll pluck your feathers and eat you for breakfast." He stamped hard on the floor.

This seemed to frighten the cuckoo, for suddenly he started up and flew for the window, only to bang his head violently against the glass and flop down on the floor again.

"Look at you, going into the glass. Silly idiot!" Hastily Gorsh got up to open the window, but the window never had been the kind to slide open at a touch, and he was still rattling the frame furiously when the cuckoo slammed into it and fell again.

Gorsh could see a little blood coming from the base of his beak.

"I'm going to open it for you, so wait a moment, won't you." With great difficulty he had just got the window open a couple of inches when the cuckoo got up and, staring hard at the eastern sky beyond the window as though he was determined to succeed at all costs this time, flew off with all his energy. This time of course, he hit the window even more violently than before and fell to the floor, where he remained perfectly still for a while. But when Gorsh put a hand out thinking to take him to the door and let him fly away, the bird suddenly opened his eyes and leaped out of the way. Then he made as though he was going to fly into the window again, so almost without thinking, Gorsh raised his leg and gave the window a great kick.

Two or three panes shattered with a tremendous crash and the window fell outside, frame and all. Through the gaping hole where the window had been the cuckoo flew out like an arrow. On and on he flew into the distance till finally he completely disappeared from sight. For a while Gorsh stayed looking out in disgust, then flopped down in a corner of the room and went to sleep where he was.

The next night, too, Gorsh was playing his cello until past midnight. He was tired and was drinking a glass of water when again there came a tapping at the door.

Whoever came tonight, he told himself, he would take a threatening attitude from the start and drive him away before the same thing happened as with the cuckoo. As he waited with the glass in his hand, a badger cub came in. Gorsh opened the door a little wider, then stamped on the floor.

"You, badger," he shouted, "d'you know what badger soup is?" But the badger seated himself tidily on the floor with a vague kind of expression and sat thinking for a while with a puzzled look and his head tilted to one side.

"Badger soup?" said the badger in a little voice. "No."

The look on the cub's face made Gorsh want to burst out laughing, but he put on a fierce expression and went on, "Then I'll tell you. Badger soup, you see, is a badger just like you boiled up with cabbage and salt for the likes of me to eat."

But the young badger looked puzzled and said, "But my father, you know, he said I was to go and study with Mr. Gorsh because he was a very nice man and not at all to be scared of."

At this Gorsh finally laughed out loud. "What did he tell you to study?" he said. "I'm busy, I'll have you know. And I'm sleepy, too."

The small badger stepped forward as though he had suddenly taken heart.

"You see, I'm the one who plays the side drum," he said, "and I was told to go and learn how to play in time with the cello."

"But I don't see any side drum."

"Here—look." The badger produced two sticks that were slung over his back.

"And what are you going to do with those?"

"Play 'The Happy Coachman,' please, and you'll see."

" 'The Happy Coachman'? What's that—jazz or something?"

"Here's the music."

This time the badger brought from behind his back a single sheet of music. Gorsh took it from him and laughed.

"Well, this is a funny piece of music! All right! Here we go then. So you're going to play the drum, are you?" He started playing, watching the cub out of the corner of his eye to see what he would do.

But the badger started busily to beat time with his sticks on the body of the cello below the bridge. He was not at all bad at it, and as he played, Gorsh found himself beginning to enjoy things.

When they got to the end, the badger stayed thinking for a while with his head to one side. At last he seemed to reach some conclusion, for he said, "When

119

you play this second string you get behind, don't you? Somehow it seems to throw me off the beat."

Gorsh was taken aback. It was true: ever since yesterday evening he'd had a feeling that however smartly he played that particular string there was always a pause before it sounded.

"You know, you may be right. This cello's no good," he said sadly. The badger looked sympathetic and thought again for a while.

"I wonder where it's no good. Would you mind playing it once more?"

"Of course I will." Gorsh started playing. The badger beat away as before, tilting his head to one side from time to time as though listening to the cello. And by the time they had finished there was a glimmering of light again in the east.

"Look—it's getting near dawn. Thank you very much." Hastily the little badger hoisted the sticks and the music onto his back, fastened them there with a rubber band, gave two or three bows, and hurried out of the house.

For a while Gorsh sat there abstractedly, breathing in the cool air that came through the window panes he'd broken the previous night, then he decided to go to sleep and get his strength back for going into town, and crawled into bed.

The next night too, Gorsh was up all night playing

his cello. It was near dawn, and he had begun to doze with the score still held in his hand when again he heard someone tapping. It was so faint that it was hard to be sure whether somebody had really knocked or not, but Gorsh, who was used to it by now, heard at once and said, "Come in."

Through a crack in the door there came a field mouse leading an extremely small child mouse. Hesitantly, she came towards Gorsh. As for the baby mouse, it was so small, only about as big as an eraser, that Gorsh couldn't help smiling. Peering about her as though wondering what he could be smiling at, the mouse set down a green chestnut in front of her and bowed very correctly.

"Mr. Gorsh," she said. "This child here is not well, and I'm afraid he may die. I beg you, out of the kindness of your heart, to cure him."

"How d'you expect *me* to play the doctor?" demanded Gorsh rather petulantly. The mother field mouse looked down at the floor and was silent for a while. Then she seemed to summon up her courage and said, "I know quite well that you cure all kinds of people very skillfully every day."

"I don't know what you're talking about."

"But it was thanks to you that the rabbit's grandmother got better, wasn't it, and the badger's father, and even that nasty old owl was cured, wasn't he, so in the circumstances I think it's very unkind of you to say you won't save this child."

"Wait a minute—there must be some mistake. I've never cured any sick owl. Though it's true I had the young badger here last night, behaving like a member of the band."

He laughed, looking down at the baby mouse in dismay.

But the mother mouse started crying.

"Ah, if the child had to get sick I only wish he'd done it sooner. To think that you were rumbling away so busily only a while ago, then as soon as he gets sick the sound stops dead, and you refuse to play any more however much I beg you. Ah, unhappy child!"

"What?" shouted Gorsh, startled. "You mean that when I play sick rabbits and owls get better? Why, I wonder?"

"You see," said the field mouse, rubbing at her eyes with a paw, "Whenever the folk around here get sick, they creep under the floor of your house to cure themselves."

"And you mean they get better?"

"Yes, it improves the circulation wonderfully. They feel so much better. Some of them are cured on the spot, others after they're back home again."

"Ah, I see. You mean that when my cello rumbles it acts as a kind of massage and cures your sicknesses for you. All right. Now I understand. I'll play for you."

He squeaked at the strings a bit to tune them, then all of a sudden picked up the mouse's child between his fingers and popped him in through the hole in the cello.

"I'll go with him," said the mother mouse frantically, jumping onto the cello. "It's the same at every hospital."

"So you're going in as well, eh," said Gorsh and tried to help her in through the hole in the cello, but she could only get her face halfway in.

"Are you all right there?" she cried to the child inside as she struggled. "Did you fall properly as I always tell you you should, with your paws all four-square?"

"I'm all right. I fell nicely," came the baby mouse's voice from the bottom of the cello, so faint it could hardly be heard.

"Of course he's all right," said Gorsh. "So we don't want you crying, now."

Gorsh set the mother mouse down on the floor, then took up his bow and rumbled and scraped his way through some rhapsody or other. The mother mouse sat listening anxiously to the quality of the sound, but finally, it seemed, she could bear the suspense no longer and said, "That's enough, thank you. Please be kind enough to take him out."

"Well? Is that all?" Gorsh tipped the cello over, put his hand by the hole and waited. Almost immediately, the baby mouse appeared. Without saying anything, Gorsh set him down on the floor. The baby's eyes were shut tight and he was trembling and trembling as though he would never stop.

"How was it? How do you feel? Better?" asked the mother mouse.

The child mouse made no reply but sat with his eyes shut, trembling and trembling for a while, then suddenly he jumped up and started running about.

"Ah, he's better! Thank you so much, sir, thank you so much." The mother mouse went and ran about a little with her child, but soon came back to Gorsh and, bowing busily over and over again, said, "Thank you so much, thank you so much," about ten times in all.

Somehow Gorsh felt rather sorry for them.

"Here," he said, "do you eat bread?"

The field mouse looked shocked. "Oh, no!" she said, looking about her uneasily as she spoke. "People do say that bread is very light and airy and good to eat—it seems they make it by kneading flour—but of course we've never been near your cupboard, and we'd never dream of coming to steal it after everything you've done for us."

"No—that's not what I mean. I'm just asking if you can eat it. Yes, I see you can. Wait a moment then, I'll give some to this boy for his bad stomach."

He set the cello down on the floor, went to the cupboard, tore off a handful of bread, and put it down in front of the field mouse.

The field mouse cried and laughed and bowed as though she had gone quite silly, then with a great show of care took the bread in her mouth and went out, shooing the child in front of her.

"Dear me," said Gorsh. "It's quite tiring talking to mice." He flopped down on his bed and was soon fast asleep and snoring.

It was the evening of the sixth day after this. With flushed faces the members of the Venus Orchestra, each carrying his instrument in his hand, came straggling from the stage of the town hall to the musicians' room at the back. They had just performed the Sixth Symphony with great success. In the hall, the storm of applause was still continuing. The conductor, his hands thrust in his pockets, was slowly pacing about among the others as though applause meant absolutely nothing to him, but in fact he was thoroughly delighted. Some of them were putting cigarettes in their mouths, some were striking matches, and some were putting their instruments away in their cases.

The clapping was still going on in the hall. In fact, it was getting steadily louder and was beginning to sound alarmingly as though it might get out of control.

The master of ceremonies came in with a large white rosette pinned on his chest.

"They're calling for an encore," he said. "Do you think you could play something short for them?"

"Afraid not," replied the conductor stiffly. "There's nothing we could do to our own satisfaction after such a major work."

"Then won't you go out and say a word to them?"

"No. Hey, Gorsh. Go and play something for them, will you?"

"Me?" said Gorsh, thoroughly taken aback.

"You—yes, you," said the concertmaster suddenly, raising his head.

"Come on, now. On you go," said the conductor.

The others thrust Gorsh's cello into his hands, opened the door, and gave him a shove onto the stage. Holding the cello, beside himself with embarrassment, he appeared on the stage, whereupon everybody clapped still more loudly as though to say, "There, you see!" Some people even seemed to be cheering.

"Just how much fun do they think they can make of a fellow?" thought Gorsh. "Right—I'll show 'em. I'll play them 'Tiger Hunt in India.'"

Quite calmly, he went out into the middle of the stage. And he played "Tiger Hunt" with all the energy of an angry elephant, just as he had done the time the cat had come. But a hush fell over the audience, and they listened for all they were worth. Gorsh ploughed steadily on. The part where the cat had given off sparks of distress came and went. The part where it had thrown itself again and again against the door also came and went.

When the work finally came to an end, Gorsh gave not so much as a glance at the audience, but, taking up his cello, made a bolt for it, just as the cat had done, and took refuge in the musicians' room. But there he found the conductor and all his other colleagues sitting quite silent, gazing straight in front of them as though there had just been a fire.

No longer caring what happened, Gorsh walked briskly past them, plumped himself on a sofa at the other side of the room, and crossed his legs.

They all turned their faces in his direction and looked at him, but their expressions were earnest and they showed no sign of laughing.

"There's something funny about this evening," Gorsh thought to himself. But the conductor stood up and said, "Gorsh, you were wonderful! The music may not be much, but you kept us listening. You've improved a lot during the past week or ten days. Why, comparing it with ten days ago is like comparing a green recruit with an old campaigner. I always knew you could if you tried, Gorsh!"

The others, too, came over to him and said, "Well done!"

"You see," the conductor was saying in the background, "he can do it because he's strong. It would kill any ordinary man."

Late that night, Gorsh went back home.

First, he had a good drink of water. Then he opened the window and, looking into the distant sky in the direction where he felt the cuckoo had gone, he said, "You know, cuckoo—I'm sorry about what happened. I shouldn't have got angry like that."

9

THE KENJU WOOD

With his kimono fastened by a piece of rope and a smile on his face, Kenju would often stroll through the woods or along the paths between the fields. When he saw the green thickets in the rain, his eyes would twinkle with pleasure, and when he caught sight of a hawk soaring up and up into the blue sky he would jump for pure joy and clap his hands to tell everyone about it.

But the children made such fun of him that in time he began to pretend not to laugh. When a gust of wind came and the leaves on the beech trees shimmered in the light so that his face could not help smiling with pleasure, he would force his mouth open and take big, heavy breaths to cover it up as he stood gazing and gazing up into the boughs.

Sometimes as he laughed his silent laugh with his mouth wide open, he would rub his cheek with his finger, as though it itched. Seen from a distance, Kenju looked as though he was scratching himself by his mouth or maybe yawning, but from close, of course, you could hear he was laughing and you could tell that his lips were twitching, so the children made fun of him just the same.

If his mother had told him to, he could have drawn as many as five hundred bucketfuls of water at one time. He could have weeded the fields, too, in a single day. But his mother and father never told him to do such things.

Behind Kenju's house, there lay a stretch of open ground, as big as the average sports field, that had been left uncultivated. One year, while the mountains were still white with snow and the new grass had yet to put out buds on the plain, Kenju suddenly came running up to the other members of his family who were tilling the rice fields, and said, "Mother, buy me seven hundred cedar seedlings, will you?"

Kenju's mother stopped wielding her gleaming new hoe and stared at Kenju.

"And where are you going to plant seven hundred cedars?" she asked.

"On the open land at the back of the house."

"Kenju," said Kenju's elder brother, "you'd never get cedars to grow there. Why don't you help us a bit with the rice field instead?"

Kenju fidgeted uncomfortably and looked down at the ground.

But just then Kenju's father straightened up, wiping the sweat off his face.

"Buy them for him, buy them," he said. "Why, he's never asked us to buy a single thing for him before. Let him have them." Kenju's mother smiled as though relieved.

Full of joy, Kenju ran straight off in the direction of the house. He got an iron-headed hoe out of the barn and began turning up the turf to make holes for planting the cedars.

His elder brother, who had come after him, saw what he was doing and said, "Kenju, you have to dig deeper when you plant cedars. Wait till tomorrow. I'll go and buy the seedlings for you."

Unhappily, Kenju laid down the hoe.

The next day the sky was clear, the snow on the mountains shone pure white, and the larks chirped merrily as they soared up and up into the sky. And Kenju, grinning as though he could scarcely repress his joy, started digging holes for the seedlings just as his brother told him, beginning at the northern edge of the land. He dug them in absolutely straight rows and at absolutely regular intervals. His elder brother planted one seedling in each hole in turn.

At this point, Heiji, who owned a field to the north of the piece of open ground, came along. He had a pipe in his mouth, and his hands were tucked inside his clothes and his shoulders hunched up as though he was cold. Heiji did a little farming, but in reality he made a good part of his living in other, not so pleasant ways.

"Hey, Kenju!" he called. "You really are stupid, aren't you, to plant cedars in a place like this! In the first place, they'll shut off the sunlight from my field."

Kenju went red and looked as though he wanted to say something, but he couldn't get it out and stood fidgeting helplessly.

So Kenju's elder brother, who was working a little way off, said, "Good morning, Heiji." He stood up, and Heiji ambled off again, muttering to himself as he went.

Nor was it Heiji alone who poked fun at Kenju for planting cedars on that stretch of grassy land. Everybody said the same things: no cedars would grow in a place like that; there was hard clay underneath; a fool was always a fool, after all.

And they were quite right. For the first five years, the green saplings grew straight up towards the sky, but from then on their heads grew round, and in both the seventh and eighth years their height stayed at around nine feet.

One morning, as Kenju was standing in front of the grove, a farmer came along to have some fun with him.

"Hey, Kenju. Aren't you going to prune those trees of yours?"

"Prune? What do you mean?"

"Pruning means cutting off all the lower branches with a hatchet."

"Then I think I'll prune them."

Kenju ran and fetched a hatchet. Then he set about mercilessly lopping off the lower branches of the cedars. But since the trees were, after all, only nine feet high, he had to stoop somewhat in order to get underneath them.

By dusk, every tree had been stripped of all its branches save for three or four at the very top. The grass below was covered with dark green branches, and the tiny wood lay bright and open.

All of a sudden it had become so empty that Kenju was upset and felt almost guilty.

Kenju's elder brother, who came back just then from working in the fields, could not help smiling when he saw the wood. Then he said good-naturedly to Kenju, who was standing there looking blank, "Come on, let's gather the branches. We've got the stuff for a fine fire here. And the wood looks much better now, too."

This made Kenju feel easier at last, and together with his brother he went in under the trees and collected together all the branches that he had cut off. The grass beneath the trees was short and neat; it looked like the kind of place where you might well find two hermits playing chess.

But the next day, as Kenju was picking the worm-eaten beans out of the store in the barn, he heard a fearful clamor over in his wood. From all directions came voices giving orders, voices imitating bugles, feet stamping the ground, then suddenly a great burst of laughter that sent all the birds of the neighborhood flying up into the air. Startled, Kenju went to see what was going on.

And there, to his astonishment, he found a good fifty children on their way home from school, all drawn up in a line and marching in step between the rows of trees.

Whichever way one went, of course, the rows of trees formed an avenue. And the trees themselves, in their green costumes, looked as though they, too, were marching in lines, which delighted the children still more. They were parading up and down between the trees with flushed faces, calling to one another as shrilly as a flock of shrikes.

In no time at all, the rows of trees had been

given names—Tokyo Street, Russia Street, Western Street. . . . Kenju was delighted. Watching from behind a tree, he opened his mouth wide and laughed out loud.

From then on, the children gathered there every day. The only times they did not come were when it was raining. On those days, Kenju would stand alone outside the grove, drenched to the skin in the rain that rustled down from the soft white sky.

"On guard at the wood again, Kenju?" people would say with a smile as they went by in their straw raincoats. There were brown cones on the cedars, and from the tips of the fine green branches cold, crystal-clear drops of rain came splashing down. With his mouth wide open Kenju laughed great breaths of laughter, standing on and on, never tiring, while the steam rose from his body in the rain.

One misty morning, though, Kenju suddenly bumped into Heiji in the place where people gathered rushes for thatching. Heiji looked carefully all around, then shouted at Kenju with an unpleasant, wolflike expression.

"Kenju! Cut your trees down!"

"Why?"

"Because they shut off the light from my field."

Kenju looked down at the ground without saying anything. At the most, the shadow of the cedars did not extend more than six inches into Heiji's field.

What was more, the trees actually protected it from the strong south winds.

"Cut them down! Cut them down! You won't?"

"No! I won't," said Kenju rather fearfully, lifting his head. His lips were tense as though he might burst into tears at any moment. It was the only time in his whole life that he had ever said anything in defiance of another.

But Heiji, who felt annoyed at being snubbed by someone as easygoing as Kenju, suddenly flew into a rage, and squaring his shoulders began without warning to strike Kenju across the face. He struck him heavily, again and again.

Kenju let himself be struck in silence, with one hand held against his cheek, but before long everything went dark and he began to stagger. At this even Heiji must have begun to feel uncomfortable, for he hastily folded his arms and stalked off into the mist.

That autumn, Kenju died of typhus. Heiji, too, had died of the same sickness only ten days before. Yet every day the children gathered in the wood just as before, quite unconcerned about such matters.

The next year, the railway reached the village, and a station was built a mile or so from Kenju's house. Here and there, great china factories and silk mills sprang up. In time, the fields and paddies all about were eaten up by houses. Almost before people realized it, the village had become a full-fledged town. Yet by some chance Kenju's wood was the one thing that remained untouched. The trees, moreover, were still barely ten feet high, and still the children gathered there every day. Since a primary school had been built right close by, they gradually came to feel that the wood and the stretch of turf to the south of the wood were an extension of their own playground.

By now, Kenju's father was quite white haired. And well he might be, for already it was close to twenty years since Kenju had died.

One day a young scholar—who had been born in what was then the village and who was now a professor in some university in America—came to visit his old home for the first time in fifteen years. Yet look as he might, he could find no trace of the old fields and forests. Even the people of the town were mostly newcomers from other parts.

Then, one day, the professor was asked by the primary school to come and give a talk about foreign countries in the school hall. When the talk was over, the professor went out into the playground with the principal and the other teachers, then walked on in the direction of Kenju's wood.

Suddenly, the young professor stopped in surprise and adjusted his spectacles repeatedly as though he doubted what he saw. Then at last he said, almost as though to himself, "Why, this is absolutely as it used to be! Even the trees are just as they always were. If anything, they seem to have got smaller. And the children are playing there. Why, I almost feel I might find myself and my old friends among them." Then abruptly he smiled, as though suddenly recalling where he was, and said to the principal, "Is this a part of the school playground now?"

"No. The land belongs to the house over there, but they leave it for the children to play on just as they please. So in practice it's become a kind of additional playground for the school, even though it's not really so."

"That's rather remarkable, isn't it? I wonder why it should be?"

"Ever since this place became built up everybody's been urging them to sell, but the old man, it seems, says it's the only thing he has to remember Kenju by, and that however hard up he is he will never let it go."

"Yes, yes—I remember. We used to think that Kenju was a bit wanting up top. He was forever laughing in a breathy kind of way. He used to stand just here every day and watch us children playing. They say it was he who planted all these trees. Ah me, who's to say who is wise and who is foolish? All one can say is that fate works in wondrous ways. This will always be a beautiful park for the children. How about it—how would it be if you called it the 'Kenju

Wood' and kept it this way forever?"

"Now, that's a splendid idea! How happy the children would be."

And so that was how it happened.

Right in the center of the grass in front of the children's wood, they set up an olive-colored slab of rock inscribed with the words "Kenju Wood."

Many letters and much money poured in to the school from attorneys and army officers and people with their own small farms in lands across the seas, all of whom had once been pupils at the school.

Kenju's family cried, they were so overjoyed.

Who can tell how many thousands of people learned what true happiness was thanks to the cedar trees of the Kenju Wood, with their splendid dark green, their fresh scent, their cool shade in summer, and the turf with the color of moonlight that lay beneath.

And when it rained, the trees would drip great, cold, crystal-clear drops onto the turf below, and when the sun shone they would breathe out clean, new air all about them, just as they had done when Kenju himself was there.

And what it was, how it happened,
right in the center of the ground in front of the
clubhouse, and they set a little olive-colored little
rock inscribed with the words "Penny Woods."

And when it glittered, the trees would dip, and
when the sun shone they would breathe too deep,
here, all about there, where they had done their
best, Penny himself was there.

Notes

The Bears of Mt. Nametoko（なめとこ山の熊）

p.7　**8** sea slugs なまこ　**8** bald sea goblins 海坊主　**9** there yawns a great cave 大きな洞穴が口をあけている　**11** waterfall 滝　**11** go thundering down ごうごうと落ちる　**12** the thick-growing cypresses and maples ひのきやいたやの茂み

p.8　**2** it is all grown over with butterbur and knotweed フキやイタドリがいっぱいに生えている　**6** rustling undergrowth ガサガサ音のする下生え　**7** in the distance 遠くで　**8** peer じっと見る　**11** in a flurry of mist 一陣の霧風となって　**13** there used to be any number of bears 昔は熊がごちゃごちゃいた　**15** liver 肝臓，胆（きも）　**19** at any rate ともかく　**20** good for the stomachache 腹痛に利く　**21** it helps wounds heal 傷をなおす　**22** the Namari hot springs 鉛の湯　**25** with their pink tongues lolling out 赤い舌をぺろぺろ出して　**26** bear cubs 子熊　**27** lose their tempers 怒り出す　**28** box each other's ears たがいの耳をなぐりあう

p.9　**1** celebrated 有名な，名高い　**3** a swarthy, well-knit, middle-aged man with a squint すがめの，浅黒いがっしりした中年男　**6** handprint 手形　**8** a cape made of bark 樹皮で作ったけら　**9** leggings きゃはん，すね当て　**9** woodsman's axe 山刀　**10** old-fashioned blunderbuss 旧式のらっぱ銃　**11** hound 猟犬　**12** crisscross 縦横に歩く　**20** burst into bloom 急に花を咲かせる　**21** ponderously のっしのっしと　**21** at home 精通して　**23** scamper 敏捷に走りまわる　**24** for all he was worth 全力を尽して，懸命に　**25** sluggish, faintly menacing backwaters のろのろした，ちょっと気味の悪い淵　**27** shake himself vigorously 身体をはげしく震わせる　**28** with nose wrinkled 鼻をしかめて

p.10　**1** catch up 追いつく　**4** in a white frieze 屏風のような白い波をたてて　**9** squelched his way ビシャビシャ音を立てて進んだ　**10** ledge 岩棚　**10** thistle あざみ　**16** for all that それにもかかわらず，それでも　**19** glint きらめき，輝き　**20** as

143

though in distress 困ったように，迷惑そうに　　**25** rear up on their hind legs 後足で立ち上がる　　**26** with both paws stretched out 両手を伸ばして　　**26** ignore 無視する

p.11　**2** forehead 額，前頭　　**2** let fly with his gun 鉄砲をぶっ放す　　**5** slump どたっと倒れる　　**6** snuffle 鼻をくんくん鳴らす　　**11** out of hatred 憎しみから　　**12** make a living 生計を立てる　　**13** with no sin attached 罪のない　　**15** authorities 当局，お上　　**17** I can't help it 仕方がない　　**17** fate 宿命，因果　　**18** make sure～ きっと～する　　**20** with a dejected air しょげた様子で　　**22** sole companion 唯一の仲間　　**24** dysentery 赤痢　　**28** razor-sharp 非常に鋭い　　**28** in one long stroke あっという間に，すうっと

p.12　**1** from under its chin down to its chest 熊のあごのところから胸へ　　**2** belly 腹　　**3** either way どっちみち　　**4** the wooden chest on his back 背中の木のひつ　　**5** drip （血が）したたる　　**6** tassels 房（ふさ）　　**11** marshy bed 沢　　**12** dusk 夕暮れ，夕方　　**14** small hut of bamboo grass 笹小屋　　**16** unlike his accustomed self いつにも似ず，柄にもなく　　**16** took the wrong trail 登り口をまちがえた　　**19** exhausted へとへとに疲れて　　**21** was half tumbled down 半分くずれかかった　　**23** spring 泉，湧水　　**26** came across～ に出くわす，（偶然）出会う

p.13　**5** were surrounded by a kind of halo 後光のようなものがさしていた　　**6** transfixed 釘付けになって　　**7** in a wheedling voice 甘えるような声で　　**22** frost 霜　　**24** shimmer ちらちら光る，ゆらめく

p.14　**5** Indian bean キササギ　　**7** innocently 無邪気に　　**11** bathed in the moonlight 月光を浴びて　　**11** stealthily そっと，こっそり　　**13** withdraw 引き下る，戻る　　**14** scent 匂い　　**14** the fragrance of spicebush くろもじの木の香り　　**17** humbled 謙虚な，かしこまった　　**21** hardware store 荒物屋，金物店　　**21** winnowing basket 唐箕，箕　　**22** whetstone 砥石　　**22** glass fly trap 硝子の蝿とり　　**24** threshold しきい

p.15　**1** brazier 火鉢　　**6** kneel ひざまずく　　**6** bow deferentially ていねいにおじぎをする　　**15** with perfect composure 落ち着きは

144

らって　　**16** palm 手のひら　　**18** brave lord of the hills 豪気な山の中の主　　**19** his face twist with anxiety 心配そうに顔をしかめる　　**20** chestnuts 栗　　**21** millet 稗（ひえ）　　**21** in the apology for～ とは名ばかりの所で　　**23** soybean paste 味噌　　**28** hemp 麻

p.16　　**1** wisteria vines 藤のつる　　**2** ～ and the like その他同種類のもの，～など　　**3** in a voice hoarse with distress 困ってしわがれ声で　　**4** whatever the price 値段はどうでも，何ぼでもいいから　　**6** puff smoke （タバコの）煙を吐く　　**7** concealing a slight grin of satisfaction うまくいったといううす笑いをそっとかくして　　**10** respectfully うやうやしく　　**12** unbend うちとける，気嫌がよくなる　　**14** glow with delight うれしくてわくわくする　　**15** at leisure ゆっくりと，のんびりと　　**16** deferentially かしこまって　　**22** immediately すぐに　　**22** a small black lacquered table 黒塗りの膳　　**23** slices of salted salmon 塩引きの鮭の刺身　　**24** chopped cuttlefish いかの切り込み　　**24** china bottle お銚子　　**26** correctly and formally ちゃんとかしこまって

p.17　　**1** gulp down のみ込む　　**1** reverently うやうやしく　　**10** it was laid down that～ ということになっていた　　**10** get the better of～ に勝つ　　**15** such being the state of affairs,～ こんな風だったから　　**20** its back hunched 背中を丸くして　　**20** clamber よじ登る

p.18　　**2** on his guard 警戒して　　**9** it just can't be helped 仕方がない　　**10** I'd rather live on chestnuts and ferns and the like 栗やシダの実のようなものでも食っていたい　　**16** without fail かならず　　**16** my insides 内臓，（特に）胃袋　　**18** filled with an odd emotion 変な気がして　　**22** stare vacantly ぼんやり見つめる

p.19　　**3** make for home 家に向う　　**7** cypress hedge ひのきの垣根　　**9** his heart gave a turn ぎょっとした，たまげた　　**15** in prayer 拝むように　　**20** wade through ～を歩いて渡る　　**22** sat spinning on the veranda in the sun 日向の縁側に坐って糸を紡いでいた　　**23** rheumy eyes 見えないような眼　　**26** straw sandals わらじ　　**26** heaved himself to his feet うんとこさと立ち上った

p.20　　**7** close-packed snow 堅雪　　**9** pant heavily ハアハアあえぐ

11 sink out of sight beyond~ の向うへ沈んで見えなくなる
16 the icicles hung in countless numbers like bead curtains つらら
らが何本も玉すだれのようにかかっていた　**18** spindle tree
ニシキギ　**21** indigo 藍色の　**21** sharply etched on ～の上に
かっきり影になって　**22** birch trunks 樺の幹　**25** confirm
たしかめる，確認する　**27** ford 浅瀬を渡る　**27** tributary
支流

p.21　**3** ridge （山の）尾根　**7** as though determined that~ と決心
しているように　**9** grimly 頑強に　**11** plateau 高原，台地
12 white marble 白大理石　**16** bark frantically はげしく吼える
19 rearing up on its hind legs 後ろ足で立って　**19** bear down
on~ を襲う　**23** turned rather pale at the sight それを見てち
ょっと顔色を変えた　**26** showed no sign of falling 倒れる様子
も見せなかった

p.22　**6** incessantly 絶え間なく　**13** phosphorescent 燐光を発する
13 the Pleiades プレアデス星団，すばる　**13** Orion's belt オリ
オン座の三つ星，参の星　**18** in a ring 環になって　**19** prostrate ひれふした　**20** like a Muslim at prayer 回教徒の祈ると
きのように　**22** corpse 死骸　**23** in a kneeling position ひざ
まずいた姿勢で　**25** chill 冴え冴えした　**26** tilt 傾く

The Spider, the Slug, and the Raccoon
（ほら熊学校を卒業した三人）

p.23　**1** slug なめくじ　**1** raccoon 狸　**4** the Badger School 洞熊学
校　**7** the race between the tortoise and the hare 兎とかめのか
けくらべ　**9** it is up to everyone to overtake his fellows だれで
も他の者に追いつかなければならない　**12** worthy りっぱな

p.24　**1** with all their might 一生懸命に　**2** vying with each other to
be top of the class クラスで一番になろうとたがいに競争して，
6 shed tears of mortification くやし涙を流した　**8** made a
mistake in calculating his marks 点数の計算をまちがえた　**10**
ground their teeth in mortification 歯ぎしりをしてくやしがった
13 it made Mr. Badger's eyes water そのため洞熊先生の目から涙

が出た　**18** graduate from〜 を卒業する　**21** mark the occasion 卒業を記念する　**23** a special farewell party for themselves 自分たちのための送別会　**26** Pooh! フン（あざけり，軽べつを表す）

p.25　**2** put〜into practice 〜を実行する　**4** sewer rat どぶねずみ　**4** enroll him in school 学校に入れる　**6** dogtooth violet カタクリ　**7** innumerable たくさんの　**9** in turn 代わるがわる　**10** golden balls of pollen 黄金色をした丸い花粉　**17** oak tree 楢の木　**20** had not a single thing of his own 自分の物は何も持っていなかった　**21** put up with his hunger ひもじいのを我慢する　**22** spin a web 網をかける，巣をかける　**24** muttered to himself ブツブツひとりごとを言った

p.26　**4** around dawn 夜あけごろ　**4** horsefly あぶ　**7** sticky ねばりけがある　**10** quite beside himself すっかり我を忘れて　**13** Mercy! ごめんなさい！　**13** piteously 哀れな声で　**15** heaved a satisfied sigh ほっと満足げに息をついた　**23** mayfly かげろう　**25** blink （眼を）パチパチさせる　**27** with an air of weariness 疲れきった様子で

p.27　**5** recite 朗唱する，歌う　**8** the dreadful tidings drear 恐ろしい報せ　**9** that's enough of that row 騒々しいことはもうやめろ，やかましい　**15** keep a firm grip on〜 をしっかりつかむ　**22** doom 悲運，死　**24** pilgrim's staff 巡礼の杖　**26** set off on a weary pilgrimage しんどい巡礼の旅に出る

p.28　**2** a-wandering from door to door 一軒一軒まわりながら　**4** alms 施し物　**4** that I may pray his soul's repose 魂の冥福を祈るために　**6** be forewarned 警戒する　**6** shun 避ける　**7** lair 巣　**8** take heed of〜 を気に留める　**9** Of webby inns beware! ＝ Beware of webby inns! 網の宿屋に気をつけろ！　**10** Enough of your impudence! 生意気はたくさんだ！　**11** in one gulp 一息で　**22** crawl about はいまわる　**26** female 雌の，女の

p.29　**3** get hold of〜 につかまる　**4** man and wife 夫婦　**12** dragonfly とんぼ　**13** pass a resolution 決議する　**14** vice-president of the Society of Insects and Worms 蟲けら会の副会長　**18** in a conceited voice 気取った声で　**20** of sons he had ten score＝he had ten score of sons 息子が二百疋　**22** incredibly 信じられないくらい　**23** like a grain of sand, no more せいぜい砂粒くらい　**25** tremendously 途方もなく　**26** good lady 夫人，奥さん　**26** console なぐさめる

p.30　**2** jealous of ～をねたんで　**7** furious 怒り狂って　**7** came down with a fever 熱病になった　**9** That cursed spider! あのいまいましいクモめ！　**9** insult 侮辱　**11** from time to time 時々　**12** lout 無骨者，田舎者　**12** stag beetle くわがた虫，かぶと虫　**17** without trace 跡形もなく，すっかり　**23** mosquito 蚊　**25** in alarm 驚いて，あわてて

p.31　**1** a great peal of laughter 大きな笑い声　**9** gnashing his teeth in rage 怒って歯ぎしりをして　**16** the rot set in 腐敗がはじまった　**19** soggy 湿気のあり，べとべとの　**22** pearlwort つめくさ　**26** handlamp ぼんぼり

p.32　**5** residence 住居，邸宅　**6** had quite a reputation 全く評判だった　**8** good-natured 人が良い　**8** considerate 思いやりのある，親切な　**9** go through hard times 困窮する　**12** butterbur juice ふきのつゆ　**15** a friend in need 困った時の友　**24** for ages 長い間　**26** I'm too starved to have the strength おなかが空いて力がありません

p.33　**1** Here, help yourself. さあおあがりなさい。　**2** thistle buds あざみの芽　**8** reluctantly しぶしぶと，仕方なく　**10** Heave-ho! よっしょ！，それ！　**10** with a crash どしんと　**28** munch down ムシャムシャ喰べる

p.34　**2** lizard とかげ　**5** medicine 薬　**10** seeing that～ であるからには，～である点から見ると　**11** dissolve 溶かす　**12** grateful 感謝して　**21** mumble もぐもぐ言う　**21** indistinctly 不明瞭に　**27** I'm feeling kind of hot around the middle おなかのあたりが何だか熱くなってきました

p.35　**2** fuss about～ を気にする，やきもきする　**3** tearfully 涙声で　**11** ridiculously 途方もなく　**12** hadn't been able to resist teasing the spider あのクモをからかわずにはいられなかった　**14** taunt あざける　**17** honorary member 名誉会員　**20** give～a contemptuous sniff ～をフンと鼻であしらう　**21** for some reason or other どういう訳だか　**22** decline（評判

が）下がる　　**23** in particular 特に　　**23** pooh-pooh any mention of~ の話が出るとヘヘンと言う　　**25** think much of~を重くみる　　**26** the way he does it あいつのやり方で　　**28** frantically 狂乱して

p.36　**6** frog 蛙　　**9** determinedly 断固として，　　**10** was longing to slup up the frog 蛙をペロリとやりたかった　　**12** drought ひでり　　**15** drank his fill たらふく飲んだ　　**18** made the very suggestion that he had been about to make himself 自分が言おうとしていた提案をしてくれた　　**20** feeble creature 弱ったやつ　　**28** purify the ring with salt 土俵を塩で清める

p.37　**6** spread-eagled 手足を広げて　　**13** opened wide his great holdall of a mouth カバンのような大きな口を一ぱいに開けた　　**16** distressing 痛ましい　　**25** buckwheat ソバ　　**28** pinkish stalks うす赤い茎

p.38　**4** on purpose わざと　　**9** pine tree 松の木　　**12** One might as well die and have done with it. もう死んでしまったほうがましだ。　　**15** Wildcat, the Blessed Feline 山猫大明神　　**16** Ave Feles なまねこ　　**22** took a bite of~ をかじった

p.39　**1** ordain 定める　　**1** ineffable 言いようのないほど大きい　　**2** decree 定める　　**3** reasonable size 適当の大きさ　　**9** such a wretch as I 私のようなつまらない者　　**12** thou sayest to chew ~ ＝you say that I should chew~　　**15** took a good mouthful of~ をムシャムシャ食べた　　**17** Ah, praise be! ああ，ありがたや！　　**21** pretend to~ のふりをする　　**22** be soaked in tears 涙でずぶぬれになる　　**23** Everything is according to thy will. みんなおぼしめしの通りです。

p.40　**1** cheat だます　　**2** pitch dark まっくら　　**4** Stop that row! やかましい！　　**5** get digested 消化される　　**7** trick だます　　**12** was performing the devotions as usual いつものように祈禱をしていた　　**14** half a bushel of unhulled rice 三升の籾（もみ）　　**15** sermon 説教　　**17** atone for~ の償いをする，罪滅しをする　　**19** Make haste to repent, else dire torment awaits you! 早くざんげをしなさい，でないとあとでえらい責苦にあいますよ。　　**21** terrified out of his wits すっかりおびえあがって　　**24** representative 代理，身代り

p.41　**1** fangs きば　**2** gouge out （目玉を）えぐり出す　**4** stare into death にらみ殺す　**6** This is by way of punishment. これは罰だ。　**7** Bear up. こらえなさい。　**9** endurance 堪忍　**20** lid ふた　**21** bundle 包み　**25** had a pricking feeling in his throat のどにちくちく刺さる感じがした　**27** each successive day 一日一日と　**28** was beside himself with pain 痛みで居ても立ってもいられなくなった

p.42　**2** swollen up ふくらんで　**6** stuffed with～ ～を詰込んで，～でいっぱいで　**8** sprout 芽を出す　**10** Dear me! ああ！　**13** swarm （ハチの）群れ　**13** hexagonal 六角形の

The Restaurant of Many Orders（注文の多い料理店）

p.43　**3** British military men イギリスの兵隊　**4** at their heels すぐ後ろに　**8** Not a bird or beast in sight. 鳥も獣も一匹も見えない。　**8** I'm just dying to let fly ぶっ放したいものだ　**12** smack in his yellow flank もろに鹿の黄色い横っ腹に

p.44　**2** flop down with a thud どたっと倒れる　**5** go astray 道に迷う　**6** worse still さらに悪いことに，その上　**7** get dizzy 目まいを起す　**8** howl ほえる　**8** foam 泡をふく　**12** casually turning its eyelids back その犬のまぶたをちょっと返して　**14** tilting his head ruefully to one side 残念そうに頭を片側に傾けて　**23** a dozen pieces' worth of game birds 10円分の小鳥　**27** no longer had the faintest idea of the way back 帰り道の見当がいっこうにつかなかった

p.45　**2** creak ギーギー鳴る　**4** I've had an awful empty feeling under my ribs for quite a while さっきから横っ腹が空腹で痛くてたまらない　**6** don't feel like walking any farther もうこれ以上歩きたくない　**9** pampas grass すすき　**13** notice 掲示　**17** civilized 文明化した，開けた　**17** Why don't we go in? 入ろうじゃないか？　**22** I'm ready to collapse with hunger. 空腹で今にも倒れそうだ　**26** in gold letters 金文字で

p.46　**1** NO ONE NEED HAVE A MOMENT'S HESITATION 決してご遠慮はいりません　**6** go wrong 思わしくいかない　**7** for

nothing ただで　　**13** corridor 廊下　　**15** PLUMP　PARTIES
AND YOUNG PARTIES ESPECIALLY WELCOME 肥った
方か若い方は特に歓迎します　　**17** were overjoyed at～ を大喜
びした　　**19** satisfy both conditions 両方の条件を充たす　　**21**
briskly 元気よく，ずんずんと

p.47　**3** appreciate 認識する，承知する　　**5** popular 評判のよい，はや
っている　　**15** screwing up his face 顔をしかめて　　**19** get
settled down 落着く　　**22** frustrating いらだたしい　　**23** long-
handled brush 長い柄のついたブラシ

p.48　**1** PATRONS ARE REQUESTED TO COMB THEIR HAIR
AND GET THE MUD OFF THEIR BOOTS HERE お客さまが
た，ここで髪をきちんとして，はきものの泥を落して下さい　　**5**
yokel 田舎者　　**6** strict on etiquette 作法に厳しい　　**7**
distinguished people 偉い人，有名人　　**10** no sooner had they
put the brush back on its shelf than it blurred and disappeared
ブラシを棚に置くやいなや，それがぼうっとかすんで消えた
12 huddle together たがいに寄り添う　　**15** fortify
themselves 防備を固める，元気をつけておく　　**20** cartridges 弾薬筒　　**22**
gun rack 銃を置く台，銃架

p.49　**3** unshoulder 肩から降ろす　　**3** unbuckle 締め金をはずす
12 hook 釘，鉤（かぎ）　　**13** pad on そっと歩く　　**14** inscription 刻んだ文字　　**15** cuff links カフスボタン　　**16** spectacles
眼鏡　　**17** pointed 尖った　　**18** black-painted safe 黒塗りの金
庫　　**20** electricity 電気

p.50　**4** clicked the lock shut ぱちんと錠をかけた　　**12** get chapped
skin ひびが切れる　　**15** be on speaking terms with the
aristocracy 貴族と近づきである　　**19** surreptitiously こっそりと

p.51　**1** I might well have got them chapped 耳にひびを切らすところだ
った　　**2** proprietor 経営者，主人　　**3** thoughtful 思慮深い
4 has got an eye for every little detail 細かい点までよく気がつく
4 incidentally ところで，ちなみに　　**6** eternal corridor どこま
でも続く廊下　　**11** perfume 香水　　**13** a shining gilt perfume
bottle 金ピカの香水のビン　　**16** smelled dreadfully like
vinegar ひどく酢のような匂いがした　　**22** the wrong stuff まち
がった物　　**26** wearisome うんざりさせる，退屈な

p.52　**4** a fine blue china salt cellar 立派な瀬戸物の塩壺　　**22** strange to say 不思議なことに　　**22** refused to budge どうしても動かなかった　　**24** carve 彫刻する　　**26** pop inside 中へ入る

p.53　**1** ogle じろじろ見る　　**6** burst into tears わっと泣き出す　　**7** furtively こそこそ　　**17** responsibility 責任　　**20** vegetable 野菜　　**21** greens 青菜，葉菜　　**24** went crumpled くしゃくしゃになった　　**24** wastepaper 紙屑　　**27** chuckle クスクス笑い

p.54　**10** woof ウーといううなり声　　**13** in a twinkling 瞬く間に，たちまち　　**17** vanish 姿を消す　　**17** as though swallowed up まるで吸い込まれるように　　**18** came a great miaowing and spitting and growling 「にゃあお，くわあ，ごろごろ」という声がした　　**21** in a puff of smoke 煙のように

p.55　**1** pant あえぐ　　**3** recovering their spirits 元気を取り戻して，元気づいて　　**8** dumpling だんご　　**11** however long they soaked themselves in hot baths どんなに長くお湯に入っても　　**14** go back to normal もとの通りになる

The Ungrateful Rat（ツェねずみ）

p.56　**4** the Underfloor Highway 床下街道　　**6** weasel いたち　　**9** sugar balls 金平糖　　**10** closet 戸棚

p.57　**1** whisker ほおひげ　　**1** twitch ピクピクする　　**2** without so much as a thank you お礼も言わずに　　**4** prick at～ をチクリと刺す　　**5** shrill 鋭い，かん高い　　**7** in astonishment びっくりして　　**9** multiple barricade 何重もの非常線　　**10** brandish 振りまわす　　**10** battle-axe まさかり　　**13** quake with fright ぶるぶる震える　　**14** Entry forbidden! 入ることを禁ずる！　　**14** sergeant-major 特務曹長　　**15** resonant 鳴り響く，朗々とした　　**21** that meek fraud of a weasel あのおとなしいいたち野郎　　**22** infuriating しゃくにさわる　　**26** sneak out of～ からちょろちょろ出る　　**27** timber shed 木小屋　　**28** grind some corn into powder とうもろこしの粒を粉にする

p.58　**9** mighty quick とても早い　　**11** pay compensation for～ の償いをする　　**15** That's nothing to do with it. それは関係ない。

17 throw people's kindness in their faces ひとの親切をさかさまにうらむ　**22** I'm sick of~ はうんざりだ　**23** namby-pamby ways めめしいやり方　**25** in a fine rage プリプリして

p.59　**2** maggot うじ虫　**4** crunched his way through~ をガリガリ食べた　**8** for want of anyone better 仕方なしに　**9** associate with~ と交際する　**10** dustpan ちりとり　**10** broom ほうき　**13** creak with the cold 寒さでギーギーきしむ　**14** before long 間もなく　**14** bedding わら　**18** fetch 持って来る　**18** while the going's good 情況が悪くならないうちに　**21** sensible idea もっともな考え　**22** without delay すぐさま, 早速　**24** plump ドシンと, ストンと

p.60　**4** felt terribly responsible for~ とても~の責任を感じた　**5** apologize わびる　**7** take advantage of the situation 形勢につけこんで, 図にのって　**13** bully 弱い者いじめ　**16** had no alternative but to return home to his nest 仕方なく巣へ帰った　**17** scared 恐がって　**21** had an upset stomach おなかが痛くなった　**24** disgusted うんざりして　**27** washing soda 洗濯ソーダ

p.61　**7** at a complete loss すっかり困って　**9** inhabitant 住民　**11** turn away hastily at the mere sight of him ねずみを見ただけで急いでわきを向いてしまう　**14** a rattrap made of woven wire 針金を編んで作ったねずみ捕り　**16** in theory 理屈では　**18** advertisement 広告　**20** disposable 使い捨ての　**20** not that~ というわけではない　**21** accord~decent treatment ~を優待する　**24** sympathy 同情　**28** mackerel サバ

p.62　**3** I'm fed up with~ はコリゴリだ　**5** fall for~ を信じ込む, ~にだまされる　**8** make off 立去る, 逃げる　**14** bait えさ　**16** fish cake 半ぺん　**24** gobble up がつがつ食う

p.63　**2** crafty ずるい　**3** sardine 鰯（いわし）　**5** hook onto~ をひっかける　**9** patronizingly 恩着せがましく　**10** swallowed his pride むっとしたのをこらえた　**13** haughtily 傲慢に, 横柄に　**20** take a bribe わいろを貰う　**21** What an insult! 無礼な！　**24** rotten 腐った　**25** fumed at the idea of being so unjustly suspected 不当な疑いを受けたので怒っていた　**28** tremendous nuisance 大変な迷惑

The Nighthawk Star（よだかの星）

p.70　**1** recover something from a thief 盗人から何かを取り返す　**15** shoot skywards 空へ飛び上る　**19** cleave the sky in two 空を二つに切り裂く　**22** force down むりに呑みこんだ　**23** shudder 身震い，戦慄　**25** reflect 反射する　**28** maw 口，咽喉

p.71　**3** gave a sudden lurch 急にドキッとした　**17** ablaze 燃えて，輝いて　**23** What brings you so unexpectedly? 何か急の御用ですか?

p.72　**2** be sure not to catch any more fish than is absolutely necessary どうしても必要な数以上の魚は取らないようにしてくれ　**7** it won't make any difference 同じことだろう　**8** give～my love ～によろしく言ってくれ　**11** give way to～ に取って代わられる　**15** combed every bit of feather and down on his body into place きれいにからだ中のはねや毛をそろえた　**19** waver 動揺する，ぐらつく　**19** persevere 辛抱する，屈せずやり通す　**22** if need be 必要あらば，事によっては　**25** the sun grew no closer 太陽は近くならなかった

p.73　**22** the constellation of Orion オリオン座　**28** pay the slightest heed to～ に少しでも注意を払う，～を相手にする　**28** insignificant 取るに足らない，つまらない，卑しい

p.75　**5** the Great Dog 大犬座　**15** disheartened がっかりした　**17** summoned up his resolve 決心した，思い切った　**18** the Great Bear 大熊座　**22** Go and cool yourself off a little. 少し頭をひやしなさい。　**25** will do nicely 役に立つだろう，十分だろう　**26** zigzag ジグザグに進む，よろよろ進む　**26** dejectedly がっかりして

p.75　**1** the Milky Way 天の川　**4** out of the question 問題外の，話にならない　**5** pompously もったいぶって，尊大に　**5** social status 身分　**9** plummet まっすぐに落ちる　**14** ruffled up his feathers 身震いして羽毛をさか立てた　**23** no bigger than～ たった～ぐらいの大きさ

p.76　**1** wheeze ハーハーいう　**1** a pair of bellows ふいご　**3** sword 剣　**3** numb しびれた，無感覚な　**8** at peace (心が) 安らいで　**9** bloodied 血のついた　**14** Cassiopeia カシオペア座

155

Wildcat and the Acorns (どんぐりと山猫)

most troublesome dispute とてもめんどうなけんか　　6 make yourself at home お楽にして下さい　　14 startled びっくりして　16 with a lordly kind of laugh 大様に笑って　　17 screwing up his face self-consciously わざと顔をしかめて　　19 be dying for～ をほしがっている　　22 crackling パチパチいう　　28 trousers ズボン

p.84　1 at the top of their voices 声をかぎりに　　8 sickle 鎌　　9 feverishly swished down～ あわてて～を刈った。　　12 clamor 騒ぐ　　17 satin しゅす，サテン　　19 worshipers 参拝者，参詣人　　20 bronze idol 青銅の仏様　　26 call it off 中止する，手を引く　　26 make up with each other お互いに仲直りする　　27 forced himself to sound important むりに威張って言った

p.85　1 set up a commotion 騒ぎを起す　　16 one had absolutely no idea what it was all about 何が何だかわけがわからなくなった　17 it was like stirring up a hornet's nest 蜂の巣をつついたようだった　　18 bawl 叫ぶ　　23 demand 尋ねる，詰問する　　25 make things up まるく収める，仲直りする　　26 whatever you say 何と言っても

p.86　7 stand on end ピンと立つ　　20 verdict 評決，裁断　　22 ridiculous めちゃくちゃな　　23 good-for-nothing 役に立たない，ろくでなしの　　23 sermon 説教　　26 with an enormous air of importance いかにも気取って

p.87　4 crackbrained 気のふれた，ばかばかしい　　6 you could have heard a pin drop 針の落ちる音が聞えるくらいだった　　8 forehead 額　　9 for sheer joy 大喜びで　　11 I'm most obliged to you. どうもありがとうございました。　　13 in not so much as a minute and a half 1分半もかけないで　　14 honorary judge 名誉判事　　16 be suitably rewarded 適当な報酬を受ける　　20 object 反対する，異議を唱える　　22 Ichiro Kaneta, Esq. 金田一郎殿　　25 twirl ひねる　　27 take courage 決心する，意を決する　　28 the wording of the card ハガキの文句

p.88　1 pertaining to certain business in hand 用事これありに付き　7 crestfallen がっかりして，しょんぼりして　　7 twiddle ひねる　11 a pint of gold acorns 黄金のどんぐり一升　　12 a salted salmon head 塩鮭の頭　　17 gold-plated ones 金メッキのどんぐ

り　　**19** scoop ひしゃくですくう　　**20** measure 枡（ます）
22 flap はためく，バタバタ動く　　**23** stretch 延びをする
23 smother a yawn あくびをかみ殺す

p.89　　**7** in a bluish haze 青っぽい霞の中で　　**10** lost their glitter 輝き
を失った，光がうすくなった　　**11** in no time まもなく　　**12**
come to a halt 止まる　　**12** plain 平凡な，あたりまえの

The First Deer Dance（鹿踊りのはじまり）

p.90　　**2** ragged でこぼこした，ごつごつした　　**3** slant down 斜めに注
ぐ　　**4** mossy plain 苔の野原　　**4** frond 葉　　**9** countryfolk
田舎の人々

p.91　　**4** settle 定住する　　**4** clear the land 土地を開墾する　　**7** local
custom 土地の習慣　　**9** bathe in the spring 温泉に入る　　**13**
limping slightly すこしびっこをひきながら　　**14** plumes（すす
きの）穂　　**16** stony wastes 石原　　**17** the mountain range
loomed large and clear 山脈のかたちが大きく，はっきりしてきた
19 pincushion 針差し，針山　　**20** with a greenish tinge 青みが
かった色で　　**21** a stand of a dozen alder trees 10本ばかりのは
んの木の木立　　**23** horse-chestnut 栃　　**25** in clump after
clump 幾むらも幾むらも

p.92　　**4** despite himself われ知らず，思わず　　**12** cotton towel 手拭
17 beyond all doubt たしかに，あきらかに　　**21** tiptoe つまさ
きで歩く　　**25** deer bain't wasting no time 鹿等はすぐに来た

p.93　　**2** the stretch of grassy turf 芝原　　**4** pampas stems すすき
7 for all the world like～ まるで～のようだ　　**9** plume 羽毛，
（すすきの）穂　　**11** sleek つやのある，なめらかな　　**12**
lowered himself onto one knee 片膝をついた　　**12** concentrate
on～ 注意を集中する　　**16** intent on～ に気がとられて，～に
専念して　　**19** what was more その上，おまけに　　**20** stagger
よろめく　　**21** as though drawn towards the center まるでまん
中へ引っぱられるように

p.94　　**1** sat himself neatly on his heels きちんと座った　　**4** every so
often 時々　　**5** foreleg 前肢　　**6** as though about to break in-

to a run 今にもかけ出して行きそうに　　**8** hooves（ひずめのある）足　　**8** thud ドサッと鈍い音を立てる　　**19** naw, 'er be dangerous＝no, it may be dangerous　　**19** better watch 'er a bit longer もう少し見てたほうがよい　　**22** when all's said and done 結局，とどのつまりは　　**27** summat＝somewhat 何だか　　**27** crittur＝creature 生きもの

p.95　**1** straightened his back 背中をまっすぐにした　　**10** stopped dead ぴたりととまった　　**15** wrinkle しわ　　**16** toadstool（一種の）きのこ　　**17** poisonous 毒のある　　**21** be getting on in years 年取った，年寄りの　　**22** sentry 番兵　　**25** Private Blue-'n-White 青白の番兵

p.96　**3** approvingly 満足げに　　**5** seemed scared to death こわくてたまらないようだった　　**6** time and time again たびたび　　**7** ready for flight 今にも逃げようと　　**8** gingerly 非常に用心深く　　**21** No telling.＝There is no telling. わからない。　　**22** in patches ぶちで，まだらで　　**24** willow leaves 柳の葉

p.97　**2** halted in his tracks in fright びっくりして途中で立止まった　　**21** pressed his nose right against it 鼻を手拭いに押しつけた　　**27** the fur on bean pods ごまざいの毛

p.98　**6** in his turn 今度は　　**7** be something of a joker かなりのおどけ者である　　**7** dangle ぶら下げる　　**9** suspicious うさんくさい，怪しい　　**13** was seized with fright 恐怖に取りつかれた　　**18** shiver 震える　　**21** what be up with 'ee?＝what's up with you? どうした？　　**22** Phew! フー，ヘー（驚き，不安，安堵など）。

p.99　**5** whatsoever 少しも　　**9** afeared＝afraid　　**10** dried-up slug ひからびたなめくじ　　**18** stab the towel with his antlers 手拭を角で突く　　**19** trample it with his hooves 足でふむ　　**25** yum＝yum-yum あーおいしい，うまいうまい　　**28** ate one mouthful of it in turn 巡ぐりに一口ずつ食べた

p.100　**7** on the point of ～ing 今にも～しようとして　　**14** drew themselves up in a line 一列に並んだ　　**17** forgetful of～ を忘れて　　**20** decline 傾く　　**25** crystal flute 水晶の笛　　**27** to and fro あちこちに

p.101　**8** shatter 粉砕する　　**9** caught his breath はっと息をのんだ

10 in its glory 絶頂にある　　**15** aglow 照り輝いて

p.102　**7** content 満足して　　**8** unnoticed ひっそりと　　**25** flee 逃げる　　**26** gale 疾風, はやて

p.103　**1** breast かき分けて進む　　**4** wake 航跡　　**6** smiled a rueful smile にが笑いをした　　**7** torn 裂けた

Gorsh the Cellist（セロ弾きのゴーシュ）

p.104　**3** moving picture house 活動写真館, 映画館　　**4** reputation 評判　　**4** none too good あまり上手でない　　**8** conductor 指揮者, 楽長　　**9** in a circle 円くならんで　　**10** backstage 楽屋で　　**10** rehearse the Sixth Symphony 第六交響曲の練習をする　　**11** were soon to perform at~ まもなく~で演奏する予定だった　　**12** blare 鳴り響く

p.105　**1** tootle away in support それを手伝ってゆるやかに鳴る　　**2** like fury 猛烈な勢いで　　**3** scrape away 弾く　　**4** oblivious to all else 他のすべてを忘れて　　**5** music 楽譜　　**9** a complete hush fell over them しんとした　　**16** tricky bit やりにくいところ　　**17** with a feeling of relief ほっと安心して　　**19** off pitch 調子はずれの　　**21** scale 音階, ドレミファ　　**22** deliberately わざと　　**23** score 譜表, 総譜　　**23** set about tuning their own instruments 自分の楽器の調子を合わせはじめた　　**24** tightened his strings 弦を締め直した

p.106　**2** scowl 顔をしかめる, いやな顔をする　　**7** look engrossed in~ に夢中になっているらしい　　**10** with a smug feeling 自己満足して　　**11** gave a great stamp 足を踏みならした　　**13** all at sixes and sevens 完全に混乱して　　**15** make a hash of~ をめちゃめちゃにする　　**17** look people in the eyes 人々の目を見る, 面目をほどこす　　**18** let some bunch of second-rate scrapers and blowers outdo us 二流の演奏家の楽団に負けてしまう　　**21** keep in perfect time with ~ とぴたっと合う　　**23** with your shoelaces dangling とけた靴ひもを引きずって　　**24** pull yourself together しっかりする　　**25** illustrious 高名な, 輝かしい　　**28** at six sharp 6時きっかりに

p.107　**11** tumbledown 荒れはてた　**11** millhouse 水車小屋　**12** on the outskirts of~ のはずれの　**13** prune （余分の）枝を切る　**15** grubs 地虫　**22** gave a shake of~ を一振りした　**24** with all the ferocity of a tiger まるで虎のような勢いで

p.108　**2** rumbling his way through~ を弾き通す　**7** bloodshot 血走った，充血した　**7** looking as though he might collapse at any moment いまにも倒れるかと思えるように見えた　**11** half-asleep ね ぼ け た　**13** tortoiseshell cat 三 毛 猫　**23** annoyance ム シ ャ ク シ ャ　**23** dam up ためる　**24** came bursting out at once たちまち突発した　**27** in the first place まず第一に

p.109　**1** What do you think you're up to? 何をしてると思っているんだ？　**3** bite at the stalks 茎をかじる　**6** droop うなだれる　**10** audience 聴衆　**11** That's enough impertinence! 生意気なことを言うな！　**14** this nuisance of a cat このうるさいネコ　**18** That's enough of your cheek! 生意気なことを言うな！　**23** ominously 不気味に，何と思ったか

p.110　**2** seriously 真面目に，すまして　**4** Would this be how it goes? それはこういうことか？　**6** tore~into strips ~を引き裂いた　**7** stuffed up both his ears tightly 自分の両耳にぎっしり詰めた　**12** collide with~ と衝突する，ぶつかる　**13** a great state of agitation 大へんな動揺状態　**17** tickle くすぐったい，ムズムズする　**18** sneeze くしゃみをする　**21** all the harder ますますはげしく　**28** in distress 困って

p.111　**2** gave off a green glow 青く光った　**7** I'll let you off now. さあこれで許してやろう。　**9** unconcerned 無関心な　**12** felt deeply aggrieved ぐっとしゃくにさわった　**12** nonchalantly 何気ない風で　**17** disdainfully 軽蔑して　**20** without warning 予告なしに，いきなり

p.112　**3** streaked off like lightning 電光石光のように走り出た　**6** as though a load had been lifted from his mind まるで心の重荷が降りたように　**11** scrub away at~ を弾く　**13** boom away 弾く　**18** scuffling つかみ合いをする

p.113　**11** distinguish 区別する　**11** as far as we cuckoos are concerned 私たちカッコーに関する限り　**23** clear off home 家へ帰る

161

27 fluttered his wings agitatedly あわてて羽ばたきをした

p.114 **1** There's no pleasing you. お前の気に入るようにすることはできない。 **3** braced himself 身構えた **3** emit（音を）発する **11** in succession 連続して，続けて **16** in time with～ に合わせて **25** be off with you 帰れ

p.115 **6** bobbing his head deferentially 頭を何べんもうやうやしく下げて **12** heaven help us いやになっちまうな **12** with a wry smile 苦笑いして **13** got quite wrapped up in things まったく夢中になった **20** the more he played the more he had the feeling that the cuckoo was better than he was 弾けば弾くほどカッコウのほうがいいような気がした **23** go on fooling around ばかなことをし続ける **26** reeled as though someone had dealt him a hefty blow on the head どしんと頭を叩かれたようにふらふらっとした

p.116 **4** resentfully 恨めしそうに **4** the least self-respecting one いちばん自尊心のないやつ，意気地のないやつ **7** cheeky 生意気な **12** scud スーッと走る **17** get away with anything 何でもやりおおせる **19** pluck your feathers 羽根をむしる **28** rattle the frame 窓わくをがたがたさせる

p.117 **5** with great difficulty やっとのことで **9** at all costs 何が何でも **19** with a tremendous crash 物すごい音をたて **25** flop down バッタリと倒れる

p.118 **5** take a threatening attitude おどすような態度をとる **8** a badger cub 狸の子 **12** with a vague kind of expression ぼんやりした顔をして **13** with a puzzled look とまどった様子で **18** burst out laughing 笑い出す，吹き出す **18** fierce 恐ろしげな，険しい **21** for the likes of me to eat おれのような者が食べるように

p.119 **2** take heart 気を取り直す，勇気づく **3** the side drum 小太鼓 **7** produce 取り出す **10** 'The Happy Coachman' 「愉快な馬車屋」 **22** beat time 拍子をとる **23** bridge（弦楽器の）こま **28** conclusion 結論

p.120 **1** second string 二番目の弦 **2** throw me off the beat 私をつまずかせる **3** was taken aback ハッとした，不意を討たれた **8** sympathetic 気の毒そうな **18** hoisted～onto his back ～を

背中にしょった　**22** abstractedly ぼんやりして　**25** get his strength back for～ のために元気を取り戻す

p.121　**5** was used to it ～に慣れていた　**7** field mouse 野ねずみ　**9** hesitantly ためらいがちに　**9** as for～ はどうかといえば、～ときたら　**10** eraser 消しゴム　**18** play the doctor 医者のまねをする　**19** petulantly むっとして　**21** summon up her courage 勇気をふるい起こす　**25** thanks to～ のおかげで　**28** in the circumstances こんな事情だから

p.122　**6** in dismay 呆れて　**10** rumble away ごうごうと鳴らす　**20** cure themselves 療す　**23** improve the circulation 血のめぐりが良くなる　**24** on the spot 即座に，その場で

p.123　**2** all of a sudden 突然　**3** popped him in ひょいと中へ入れた　**13** with your paws all four-square 足をそろえて　**21** bow 弓　**22** rhapsody ラプソディ　**23** listening anxiously to the quality of the sound 心配そうにその音の工合を聞いて　**25** suspense 不安，気がかり　**27** tip～over ～をひっくり返す

p.124　**21** knead flour 小麦粉をこねる　**22** cupboard 戸棚

p.125　**5** with a great show of care とても大事そうに　**7** shooing the child in front of her 子供を先に立てて　**10** snore いびきをかく　**13** straggle ばらばらに来る　**16** storm of applause 嵐のような喝采　**20** thoroughly すっかり，全く　**24** clapping 拍手　**25** steadily 着々と，段々と　**26** get out of control 手におえなくなる

p.126　**1** the master of ceremonies 司会者　**2** rosette ばら花飾り　**3** encore アンコール　**5** Afraid not. できません。　**6** to our own satisfaction 満足がいくように，気が済むように　**11** thoroughly taken aback すっかり呆気にとられて　**12** concertmaster コンサートマスター　**16** gave him a shove onto the stage 舞台へゴーシュを押し出した　**17** with embarrassment 困って，きまり悪くて　**22** make fun of～ をばかにする　**28** a hush fell over the audience 聴衆はしいんとなった

p.127　**2** plough on 骨折って進む　**6** gave not so much as a glance at the audience, but made a bolt for it 聴衆の方は見もせず，楽屋へ向って急いだ　**9** took refuge in～ に避難した　**10** colleague 仲間，同僚　**14** plumped himself on～ にどしんと座った

163

18 showed no sign of laughing 笑っているようではなかった
25 green recruit 新兵　　**25** old campaigner 古参兵，古つわもの
p.128　**1** in the background 向うの方で

The Kenju Wood（虔十公園林）

p.129　**4** stroll ぶらぶら歩く　　**5** thicket やぶ，茂み　　**10** in time そのうちに　　**11** pretend not to laugh 笑わないふりをする

p.130　**4** cover it up それを隠す，ごまかす　　**5** bough 大枝　　**8** as though it itched さも痒いように　　**9** scratch himself by his mouth 口の横わきを搔く　　**10** from close 近くからは　　**15** as many as five hundred bucketfuls of water 五百杯もの水　　**19** a stretch of open ground 一面の野原　　**20** had been left uncultivated まだ耕地になっていなかった　　**25** till the rice fields 田んぼを耕す，田打ちをする　　**26** cedar seedlings 杉苗　　**27** wield a hoe 三本鍬をふるう

p.131　**7** fidget uncomfortably きまり悪そうにもじもじする　　**9** straighten up 背を伸ばす　　**16** iron-headed hoe 唐鍬　　**25** chirp 鳴く，さえずる　　**27** repress his joy 喜びを抑える

p.132　**3** at absolutely regular intervals 実にきちんと間隔をおいて　　**7** his hands were tucked inside his clothes ふところ手をして　　**16** get it out ことばを発する　　**20** amble off のっそり行く　　**22** poke fun at～ を嘲笑する　　**25** clay 粘土　　**28** green sapling 青い苗木

p.133　**5** grove 林　　**11** hatchet 山刀　　**14** mercilessly 無慈悲に，片っぱしから　　**14** lop off （枝を）払う　　**18** had been stripped of～ を払い落されていた　　**19** save for～ を除いて　　**20** layer 層，重ね　　**23** guilty 気がとがめる，胸が痛い　　**26** good-naturedly きげんよく　　**27** looking blank ぼんやりした顔をして　　**28** the stuff for a fine fire 焚きもの

p.134　**7** the kind of place where you might well find two hermits playing chess 仙人が碁でもうっていそうな所　　**9** worm-eaten 虫喰いの　　**12** bugle （軍隊などの）ラッパ　　**18** all drawn up in a line 集って１列になって　　**19** in step 歩調をそろえて　　**21**

164

whichever way one went どちらを通っても　　22 avenue 並木
道　　23 costume 服　　26 with flushed faces 顔をまっ赤にして
27 as shrilly as a flock of shrikes モズのようにかん高い声で

p.135　8 drenched to the skin ずぶぬれになって　　10 on guard at～
で立番して　　11 straw raincoat 蓑（みの）　　12 cone 球果,
実　　14 splash ポタポタたれる　　19 bump into～ に出会う
20 rushes for thatching 屋根葺き用のかや

p.136　7 in defiance of～ に逆って　　9 snub 鼻であしらう，ばかにす
る　　10 easygoing 人のいい，のん気な　　18 stalk off のしりの
しりと歩いて行く　　20 typhus 発疹チフス　　23 unconcerned
about～ に無関心で，～に構わずに　　26 china factory 陶器工
場　　26 silk mill 製糸工場

p.137　1 full-fledged 十分に発達した　　8 extension 延長，続き　　13
professor 教授　　15 for the first time in fifteen years 15年ぶり
に　　15 look as he might どこを見ても　　16 find no trace
of～ の形跡もない　　23 principal 校長　　26 adjusted his spectacles repeatedly 何度も眼鏡を直した

p.138　5 abruptly 突然　　10 in practice 実際問題として　　10 a kind
of additional playground 附属の運動場のようなもの　　13
remarkable 驚くべき，立派な　　16 urge しきりに促す，説得す
る　　18 however hard up he is どんなに困っても　　21 a bit
wanting up top 少し足りない　　26 fate works in wondrous
ways 運命の作用は不思儀だ

p.139　6 set up an olive-colored slab of rock inscribed with the words
"Kenju Wood" 「虔十公園林」と彫った黄緑色の石碑を建てた
9 attorney 検事　　9 army officer 将校　　12 were so overjoyed ほんとうに喜んだ

（東京都立北多摩高等学校教諭　瀬戸武雄）

N.D.C. 909   165p   15cm

WILDCAT AND THE ACORNS
and other stories

1985年 9月20日   第 1 刷発行
1996年 7月17日   第 8 刷発行

著　者　宮沢賢治

訳　者　ジョン・ベスター

編　集　講談社インターナショナル株式会社

発行者　野間佐和子

発行所　株式会社講談社
　　　　〒112-01　東京都文京区音羽2-12-21
　　　　電話　販売部　東京 03-5395-3626
　　　　　　　製作部　東京 03-5395-3615

　　　　講談社インターナショナル株式会社
　　　　〒112　東京都文京区音羽1-17-14
　　　　電話　編集部　東京 03-3944-6493

組 版 所　小宮山印刷工業株式会社
印 刷 所　豊国印刷株式会社
製 本 所　株式会社堅省堂

定価はカバーに表示してあります

ISBN4-06-186015-1　　　　　　　　　（インター）

WILDCAT AND THE ACORNS
and other stories

ISBN4-06-186015-1